An eating disorder, wheth[er] anorexia nervosa or a food and weight obsession, is usually a guilty and secret problem. Although now medically recognised, treatment is often one-sided, with psychiatrists, physicians and nutritionists often taking very different approaches.

Paulette Maisner, for many years herself a compulsive eater, managed to effect a personal cure. Recognising that her approach might be of value to other sufferers, she set up the Maisner Centre. Her aim was to amalgamate many approaches into a comprehensive and effective individual programme of treatment that helps to break the vicious circle of an eating disorder.

This is very much a self-help book, based on self-awareness and improved self-image with emphasis on the practical steps anyone with an eating disorder can take to help themselves. It is a book that will also be of value to the family and friends of a sufferer in helping them to understand the nature and conflicts of the problem.

The Maisner Centre for Eating Disorders is at:

P.O. Box 464,
Hove,
East Sussex.
BN3 2BN
Telephone: Brighton (0273) 729818/29334

Paulette Maisner now has consulting
rooms in the City of London and South
West London and there are also many
branches of The Maisner Centre throughout
the country. Details of your local branch,
postal courses and consultations are
available by sending a large stamped
addressed envelope to the above address.

THE FOOD TRAP

A Self Help Plan to Control
Your Eating Habits

PAULETTE MAISNER
with ROSEMARY TURNER

UNWIN
PAPERBACKS

LONDON SYDNEY WELLINGTON

First published in Great Britain by Allen & Unwin, 1985

First published in paperback by Unwin® Paperbacks, an
imprint of Unwin Hyman Limited in 1986
Reprinted 1988

UNWIN HYMAN LIMITED
15-17 Broadwick Street
London W1V 1FP

Allen & Unwin Australia Pty Ltd
8 Napier Street, North Sydney, NSW 2060, Australia

Allen & Unwin New Zealand Pty Ltd with the Port Nicholson Press
60 Cambridge Terrace, Wellington, New Zealand

ISBN 0–04–613064–0

British Library Cataloguing in Publication Data
Maisner, Paulette
  The food trap: a self help plan to
  control your eating habits.
1. Appetite disorders—Treatment
I. Title II. Turner, Rosemary
616.85′2   RC552.A72
ISBN 0–04–613064–0

Printed in Great Britain by
The Guernsey Press Co. Ltd., Guernsey, Channel Islands

Contents

Acknowledgements

To my son Peter with love and affection, to Gabriel Duffy without whose support this book would not have been possible, to Frances Kelly my friend and agent, and to all the clients of the Maisner Centre past and present.

And to Dolly with special love.

The Author wishes to thank Northern Songs Limited, ATV Music, 19 Upper Brook Street, London W1, for their kind permission to reproduce material from *Eleanor Rigby* by John Lennon and Paul McCartney.

Preface

'Elvis's immense bulk is owing entirely to the eating habits that he developed as a child under his mother's loving care. He gorges himself with food at every time of day or night. Concealed in his clothes closet is a full-sized refrigerator kept stocked with snacks for those abrupt and unpredictable attacks of the "munchies" that beset speed freaks. Sometimes he seeks to curb the ill-effects of his between-meal noshing by stocking his box entirely with yogurt. This tactic avails him nothing, because after lapping up a couple of containers of sweet, luridly-coloured pap, instead of feeling his appetite sated, he experiences the deep arousal of true hunger. Then, nothing can stop his compulsive gobbling, until he has emptied twenty or thirty of the waxy boxes. Or, suppose he confines himself to healthful fruit: some fine ripe honeydew melons.

Drawn like a giant bear to the honey in the heart of the melon, he'll cut into and scoop out the oozing pulp in a trice, not stopping until he has put away six or eight of the massive fruits. Or, if his sweet tooth is really aching, he will ring up his valet, Hamburger James, at three in the morning and send him out to buy at some all-night market a hundred dollars worth of popsicles. As the rest of the world is brewing coffee and frying eggs, James will be toting up to his master's lair a huge bowl of Eskimo Pies, Fudgesicles, Dreamsicles, and Nutty Buddys. Next afternoon, the bowl will be back in the kitchen full of dry, stained sticks.'

From Elvis by Albert Goldman
Penguin Books Ltd

Introduction

In recent years thousands of books have been written on how to lose weight, a million diets have been published, but the market for such books grows bigger instead of smaller. If you have an eating problem you have probably tried every diet – and failed, followed every weight reduction plan – and put it all back on again. So why yet another book about eating?

This book does not present an easy way to get slim. It does not come up with a miracle way to instantly overcome your compulsive eating. Addiction to food is a twentieth-century epidemic, and beating the problem means committing yourself to a lot of hard work, self-analysis and self-discipline. Very rarely is there one single cause of an eating problem; it is brought about by a combination of factors, both physical and emotional. Social attitudes and upbringing also have a strong bearing on a person's attitude to food. If you want to overcome your eating problems you have to be prepared to make some drastic changes in your life.

What is offered here is a plan to help the compulsive eater get herself out of her bad eating habits. The more effort and dedication that is put into following the plan, the greater the chances of success. Simply reading the book and putting it away on a shelf will do no good at all. This plan *will* work for you, but you have to do all the hard work yourself.

The plan for overcoming compulsive eating habits has been put together as a result of three years work with compulsive eaters at the Maisner Centre for Eating Disorders in Brighton. Thousands of people, mainly women, have contacted the Centre. Many went into the project wholeheartedly and made an enormous effort to overcome their problems and succeeded. A few admitted that it all seemed too much like hard work and gave up.

Paulette Maisner, who founded the Centre and deals

personally with all those who come for help, believes that anyone who really wants to get over their eating problems can succeed, but there are many people who prefer to hide behind their compulsive eating because it is easier than facing up to more difficult problems in their lives. Recognising your true motives is an important part of the plan to overcome your eating problem.

Paulette spent thirty years battling with her eating problems, what she describes as 'looking for the easy way out'. When she finally discovered how to get her eating under control, she decided to devote herself to the job of helping others to find their own way out of the food trap. She is the motivation behind the success of many of her most difficult cases, an inspiration to anyone with an eating problem, because, however rough a path they are treading, she has been that way herself and knows only too well the difficulties and hardships to be faced.

All the case histories included in this book are true, but for reasons of confidentiality the names and professions have been changed.

CHAPTER ONE

The First Step

It is the first step which is troublesome.
French proverb

Do you have an eating problem? If you are reading this book the answer is probably yes, but exactly what is your problem, and what do you need to know to control it? Many people don't realise they are compulsive eaters, though some are serious cases. They are aware they have a problem with their eating, but have no idea how deeply it is affecting them at all levels – physically, mentally and psychologically. The shame that always accompanies eating problems prevents most compulsive eaters from telling their closest friends or even their husbands. They do not know how to get help and cannot go to their doctor.

What is a compulsive eater?

There are a number of different types of compulsive eater, and every type has its mild and serious cases. It is not easy to give a simple picture because there are so many different ways of suffering from the problem, no two people suffer in exactly the same way.

Compulsive eating is not necessarily a state of continual bingeing, but its more serious effects manifest as fear of food and obsession with eating and not eating that prevents the person leading a normal life. Because the compulsive eater thinks about food all the time, she is trapped in a cage of her own thoughts. The compulsive eater has much in common with the alcoholic: she will not admit that anything is wrong, even to herself, until she is at rock bottom. So the first step is to admit to

1

yourself that you have a problem and to face the fact that it will not go away by itself. It will be hard work, but well worth it, to get your eating under control.

Compulsive eating rarely disappears entirely. It can however be controlled so you can live a happy and fulfilling life with the door of the cage open instead of locked shut. After treatment for cancer it is many years before the doctors pronounce the patient cured, and similarly with eating problems, once 'cured' they may seem to have disappeared but can flare up again at times of extreme stress.

PAULINE was a compulsive eater for many years until she eventually managed to get on top of the problem and regarded herself as cured. Then four years after her last binge she had to have all her teeth removed and the result of that traumatic experience was 24 hours of bingeing. But because she had devoted much time and hard work to learning to deal with her eating problems, after that initial 24 hours she got her eating under control again.

Once your eating is under control you can live with the confidence that you are on top of the problem and know that if it does break out again it will never be quite so bad and you will know how to deal with it. By following this course you will learn to enjoy controlling your eating, so although it can be a permanent disorder, always lurking in the background, you will not slide back into the despair of being an uncontrolled compulsive eater.

Compulsive eating is not a matter of continually eating too much because you love food and enjoy eating, although this may be the popular view of the problem. If this sounds like you, then your problem is more likely to be greed; either develop more self-discipline or carry on being content to be fat and happy. Compulsive eating has little to do with the amount you eat. It is the fact that eating bothers you that makes it an illness. Can compulsive eating be called an illness? Although the medical profession might not classify it as such, anyone suffering from this problem is certainly not healthy in either body or mind. So, in this book, compulsive eating is viewed as an illness.

Compulsive eating involves a lot of unhappiness – not just regret when the scales show a few extra pounds, but a whole range of distressing emotions such as guilt, loneliness, lack of confidence, fear of failure, and a generally poor self-image. Some people turn to alcohol to drown their troubles, others to drugs, to violence, to crime or to suicide. The compulsive eater turns to food; she is helplessly addicted to cramming food into her mouth.

The vast majority of compulsive eaters, and certainly of those approaching the Maisner Centre for help with their problem, are women. It does seem to be a problem that hits women harder than men for all sorts of reasons, apart from the obvious ones such as women being more involved with food in their everyday lives. For this reason a compulsive eater is generally referred to as 'she' in this book, but most of the information given applies equally to any male compulsive eaters.

What is a binge?

Most people describe binge-eating as a time when their eating is out of control. Different people have different ideas about exactly what makes up a binge. The quantity of food eaten is not usually relevant; it is the emotions involved that count. If eating causes physical and emotional distress it can be termed a binge; mindless eating of food, unplanned eating, are all signs of a compulsion. Some binges are made up of vast amounts of food, in fact anything that is to hand is swallowed until the stomach is overstretched and uncomfortable. For others two biscuits constitutes a binge because they have set themselves a hopelessly high standard of diet which they have momentarily failed to live up to. Some only turn to food at times of great stress. They may go for months without a binge and their eating problem only shows itself in a crisis. Others binge daily because not only their eating, but their whole life has slipped out of control.

Why eat if it causes distress?

This is the question every compulsive eater must ask herself. Only when she can give a satisfactory answer can she begin to get her eating under control. If only small amounts of food are

3

involved in binges, this can be a stress problem rather than an eating problem. Some people can get incredibly upset if they eat one biscuit; they suffer anxiety and fear as they nibble it and are aware of the panic building up. Such small amounts do not really affect weight, they are the sort of thing someone without an eating problem would eat without giving it a second thought. The anxiety of such a binge is way out of proportion to the amount of food eaten.

CAROLE is a compulsive eater who is so obsessed with her weight and her eating that she eats nothing but an apple and green salad all day, but as soon as she finds herself under any kind of stress she binges. She suffers a lot from stress and emotional problems, but tends to blame all her problems on her eating rather than on the true cause which is her high pressure job.

On one occasion Carole binged on cheese. She had a block of cheese from which she kept slicing off paper-thin pieces and eating them with all the accompanying anxiety, panic and guilt familiar to the binger. Emotionally she suffered terribly, and yet the total amount of cheese she consumed was only about one ounce, hardly enough to make any great difference to a diet. In this case nearly all Carole's eating problems are a direct result of stress and will not disappear until she has sorted her life out.

What is bulimia nervosa?

As far as this book is concerned, people suffering from bulimia nervosa are those compulsive eaters who make themselves vomit after food. Many compulsive eaters also abuse diuretics and laxatives. Not all compulsive eaters are bulimics, but all bulimics are compulsive eaters, and there are as many causes of bulimia nervosa as there are sufferers.

Most bulimics are underweight, some are only about half a stone over their ideal weight, but there are still many who are greatly overweight, proving this is not a successful way of getting slim. When they binge they immediately dislike the feeling of fullness and have to get rid of the extended feeling in their stomach. In severe cases this can quickly be followed by yet another urge to binge. Sometimes the bulimic is bingeing and vomiting up to 18 times a day. Like most compulsive eating habits, all this is indulged in in privacy and unobserved, so even husbands and family may not realise what is going on and how serious the situation is.

JENNY is the mother of a small boy. At one point the child became very distressed, but all he would say was that his mother was dying. Eventually it was discovered that his mother was a bulimic, and because the child had heard his mother vomiting so frequently behind the closed bathroom door, he had assumed she was very ill and therefore must be dying.

How does bulimia nervosa start?

It often starts with a dislike of feeling over-full after eating too much. The sheer physical discomfort prompts the person to vomit up what she has eaten, and she, mistakenly, assumes that by doing this she can avoid becoming fat. Usually she tells herself she will just do it once in an extreme situation, but it is surprising how easily it becomes a habit. Often people catch on to the idea after they have been sick from drinking too much; they realise this is a good way to alleviate an uncomfortable feeling in the stomach. Slimming clubs can inadvertently encourage people to become bulimic. The pressure is on to lose weight each week or face public humiliation, and if a person has binged she is desperate to get rid of the extra weight before her next club session.

The Romans were famed for their vast and lengthy banquets, where guests ate until they were full, then retired behind specially placed screens to vomit up the contents of their stomachs to make room for the next course. This was done much more through greed than for the largely emotional reasons behind the behaviour of anyone suffering from bulimia nervosa.

Is it a dangerous habit?

Very dangerous. Once you start it becomes very difficult, if not impossible, to stop, even to the point where the stomach automatically rejects any food offered. If you suffer from bulimia nervosa you should seek medical help without delay. Serious side effects can occur, and often the first signs of these are in the teeth. Dentists should be on the look out for women patients who suddenly develop a lot of tooth erosion; this is caused by the acid in the vomit. Also, hair can lose its texture and fall out, and there can be tearing and bleeding in the throat. Another common side effect is severely infected salivary glands which may lead to swellings in the neck, and may ultimately require surgery. Hiatus hernia is another common problem for bulimics, and the stomach and intestines may begin to break down and cease to function efficiently, leading to a variety of intestinal abnormalities. The kidneys may be affected too, especially if too many diuretics are used, resulting in kidney infections and even total failure of the kidneys in some cases. The bulimic may hide behind dark glasses because of bloodshot eyes from the strain of vomiting. Her menstrual periods may stop due to stress and undernourishment, even if the person is not underweight. Excessive vomiting can lead to epileptic fits or even heart attacks.

Nearly all bulimics have swollen stomachs; however much they diet to flatten their stomach, the bulimia only makes it worse. Think how starving children in Africa are pictured with swollen bellies; the undernourished bulimic is suffering in a similar way. By vomiting food before it has begun to be absorbed or by taking laxatives to speed food through the system, essential nutrients are not being taken up by the body, resulting in malnutrition. Potassium loss in particular leads to sugar craving, which in turn leads to more bingeing and the vicious circle goes round yet again.

'I only make myself vomit occasionally'

It is a habit which, once started, tends to snowball. Perhaps you have got your eating fairly under control at the moment. If suddenly a lot of pressures build up and you begin to lose control, you could find yourself getting into the bingeing and vomiting habit more and more.

Psychological problems such as guilt, shame, worthlessness and helplessness grow the more you give in to the bulimic tendency. Such emotions were probably there in the first place, giving rise to the original eating problems, but the bulimic habit allows them to grow and take over your life.

Some bulimics are swallowing up to 30,000 calories a day, and that costs a lot of money. One question you have to ask yourself is, can I afford to be a bulimic? If you only binge once a week, you might be able to pay for it, but what if it creeps up to every day? It can be a cripplingly expensive addiction. It is hardly surprising that many bulimics steal at some time.

Some bulimics only need to eat a small amount of food to feel so uncomfortably full that they have an urgent need to get rid of it all. Some drink orange juice or eat beetroot before a binge, so they will be able to recognise when the last food in their stomach has been ejected. They are driven by some idea of cleansing themselves internally by vomiting food and taking laxatives. Usually the habit builds up slowly until it becomes a regular part of their life. They lose the capacity to eat a full meal, feeling uncomfortable after only small quantities of food, so it is essential for bulimics to eat a number of small meals rather than one or two larger meals a day.

There are some bulimics who behave in this way to hold others to ransom. They learn that it is a powerful means of getting their own way because it is very distressing for others to see. These people are almost impossible to cure because they do not really want to be helped; they thrive on having everyone running around them in circles. However, most bulimics are well groomed, bright, vivacious people; nobody suspects they have this distressing problem because they are so good at hiding it.

MARY had been an anorexic and developed the compulsive eating habit and bulimia nervosa. Her mother was obsessed about Mary's weight and eating habits, and Mary played on this, getting her way in everything by threatening to be sick. If she wanted to go out and her mother said no, she would threaten to make herself sick until her mother gave in. She was a girl who did not want to get better because she enjoyed the power her bulimia gave her over her mother.

Do you really want to control your eating?

Everyone has to take responsibility for themselves and for their own eating. Are you ready to do something about your eating? It is a full-time job and if you do not feel ready to tackle it at the moment, wait until you feel able to make a really positive effort. To start half-heartedly and give up before you have achieved any success will only lead to a sense of failure, guilt and a lowering of self-esteem. On the other hand there will always be some good excuse for putting off making a start on something as difficult as getting your eating under control. Perhaps Christmas is coming up, then it is always more difficult to think about dieting in the winter, you'll wait until the summer, but not until after your summer holiday ...

If you really feel your eating is out of control and casting a blight on your life, make the decision *today* that you are going to do something about it, and take the first step. If you really want to be slim, it is worth making the effort. Nothing is achieved without working for it, whether it is passing A levels or becoming a champion skater; all such achievements involved hours of dedication, and so does having a trim healthy figure.

Controlling your eating problem takes discipline. It means you cannot eat just what you want, whenever you want it. But the discipline and control you need to achieve that desired figure will also improve the quality of your life in every other way. If you are out in the street and feel an urge to go to the toilet, you have the control to wait until you reach the proper place. The same control should apply to eating habits. If you are going out for a long time, have a meal before you go and wait until you get back to eat again, or plan a meal or snack out during the day, leaving no reason to indulge in unplanned eating. Don't be tempted to grab a chocolate bar in the street.

JANICE travelled down to Brighton by train from Nottingham to visit the Maisner Centre. She arrived early in the morning having eaten nothing since the night before, refused an offer of lunch and travelled back the same day without eating. When she got home she had a huge binge. She was of course hungry after a busy day and no food for 24 hours so the binge was inevitable.

She would have been better able to avoid the evening binge if she had planned her day's eating sensibly, with a breakfast before she left home, perhaps a salad lunch at the station and some fruit and cheese to eat on the train. With a sensible meal on arriving home this would have totalled less calories than her binge on an empty stomach.

Thinking ahead is important when trying to control your eating habits. Don't always assume you will have the opportunity to eat properly when you get hungry, or that you won't get hungry in several hours' time. For example if you are going to the cinema straight from work, don't assume the people you are with will want to eat before the film; they may want to wait until afterwards. Have something to eat at work in case this happens, otherwise you may find yourself eating ice cream and chocolate in the cinema because you are hungry.

'When I am slim, I will be able to handle my eating problems'

Do not allow yourself to believe that all your other problems will disappear like magic once you are slim. Don't wait until you have a perfect figure to buy a new dress or join an exercise class or do something about your eating problems. And don't fall into the trap of thinking that thin equals happiness. These are myths, but very commonly believed among compulsive eaters.

It is often the case that once the other problems in a person's life have been sorted out, the eating binges disappear or become much more controllable. But compulsive eaters are frequently so obsessed with food that they are unable to focus on anything else in their lives. Now, however, is the time to try.

Have you ever really asked yourself just how different your life would be if you weighed a few pounds less? If you are within half a stone of your ideal weight try answering the following questions. Write down your answers and look at them again in six months' time to see if your attitude has changed at all.

1 How did you work out what you consider to be your ideal weight?

2 Did you look at a number of charts or just one? ('Ideal weights' can vary up to a stone.)

3 Is your ideal weight below that generally given by charts because you want to allow yourself room for bingeing, special occasions like Christmas or holidays etc?

4 What difference do you think it would make to your life if you were at your ideal weight?

5 Will your children/husband/parents/boy-friend love you more if you weigh a few pounds less?

6 Would your job be less boring if you weighed a few pounds less?

7 Do you think your day-to-day chores would become less tedious if you did not have to worry about your weight?

8 Do you think that if you weighed a few pounds less the ideal job/partner would come along?

9 Do you think your financial situation would improve?

10 Do you think you would be less lonely if you weighed slightly less?

11 Do you think your boss would treat you more favourably?

12 Do you think your pre-menstrual tension would ease if you weighed less?

13 Do you think losing a few pounds would prevent a member of your family from becoming ill?

14 Do you think you will find your school/university/work easier?

Recognising the pattern

The next step is to try and find out if you are a compulsive eater? Answer the questions in Chart 1.1. Too many ticks in the 'yes' column means that you do have an eating problem. Read every question carefully and think about your reply; it will tell you a great deal about yourself and your eating habits. The questions are compiled from many of the comments compulsive eaters make about themselves, and will show you if you have anything in common with others who have eating problems. Put aside a time when you can be alone and concentrate on filling in the answers to the questions; simply taking the time to do this is therapeutic in itself.

The weekly charts

Now you are ready to begin filling in the weekly analysis charts (see Chart 1.2). Make plenty of copies of this chart either by hand or using a photocopier, so that you have no excuse for not continuing to keep a record of your eating. This may seem like a lot of hard work, but there is no easy answer to eating problems and you must be prepared to make a real effort if you truly wish to overcome yours. In Part I of the chart fill in an appropriate square every time you binge (if you binge more than ten times between the same hours in one week add on more squares). Every part of the chart should be filled in daily or each time you binge to help you build up a pattern of your eating. For example, you may discover a column of filled-in squares builds up in the 10–11 am slot which will show you this is your danger hour for bingeing.

In Part II put a tick or a cross against the place where you did your unplanned eating, again do this for each binge and a pattern may begin to emerge. The same applies for each of the other sections, putting your tick or cross against the appropriate answer.

This chart is an analysis of your bingeing, that is of food you have eaten which you did not plan to eat, and it does not include your planned meals. It is designed to give you a picture of when, where and why you are bingeing so that you can then go on to tackle the reasons for it. Perhaps you find you only binge when you are alone, in which case you may need to look more closely at how you handle loneliness.

If you only binge occasionally it may take some time before you see a pattern emerging, but if you binge daily it should become clear fairly quickly. Compulsive eating may be caused by trigger foods, trigger places, trigger people or trigger moods, but it is usually a combination of two or three of these that fires you off on a binge. Filling in the charts regularly and honestly will begin to show you which are your triggers.

Chart 1.1 *Are you a compulsive eater?*

Please tick the appropriate boxes:

	Sometimes	Yes	No
1. a. Do you have panic desires for certain foods?			
b. Do you recognise real physical hunger?			
c. If you do, do you eat when you are not hungry?			
d. Are you fully aware of what you eat?			
2. Do you look forward with pleasure and anticipation to the moment when you can eat alone?			
3. Do you eat sensibly before others and make up for it alone?			
4. Do you have feelings of guilt and remorse every time you eat?			
5. Do you have feelings of guilt and remorse every time you over-eat?			
6. Do you plan your secret binges ahead of time?			
7. If you were eating a cake or sweets, could you eat only half and leave the rest? (eg, could you leave, say, half a Mars bar?)			
8. Do you enjoy cooking for others, although you do not enjoy eating what you have cooked?			
9. Do you avoid socialising because of your inability to cope with food?			
10. Do you find it difficult to refuse food when pressed?			
11. When eating with others, do you eat the same as everyone else because you are embarrassed to ask for what you know is better for you?			
12. Do you feel awkward when eating with others?			
13. Are your table manners the same when you eat alone as they are when you eat in public?			
14. Are you able to leave food on your plate?			
15. Are your eating habits costing you an excessive amount of money?			
16. Are you ever afraid to weigh yourself?			
17. Do you think about food and your weight constantly?			
18. Does your well-being depend on whether you have a 'good' eating day or 'bad' eating day?			

Add your score as follows:

		Sometimes	Yes	No
1.	a.	1	2	0
	b.	1	0	2
	c.	1	2	0
	d.	1	0	2
2.		2	4	0
3.		2	4	0
4.		2	4	0
5.		2	4	0
6.		2	4	0
7.		2	0	4
8.		2	4	2
9.		2	4	0
10.		2	4	0
11.		2	4	0
12.		2	4	0
13.			0	4
14.			0	4
15.			4	0
16.			2	0
17.			4	0
18.			2	0

Now answer these questions and add them to your score:

Put the relevant number in the appropriate box and add numbers to your total score

1. How many slimming magazines have you read in the last few months?
2. How many diets have you tried in the last 12 months?
3. By how many pounds has your weight fluctuated in the past 12 months in an excess of 5lb, not including premenstrual days?
4. How many times have you joined a slimming club?
5. How many times a week do you weigh yourself?

What your score means:

Score of 0–10 It is obvious you do not have an eating disorder of any description. Lucky you!

Score of 10–50 It is most likely you are suffering to a certain degree with an eating disorder, whether or not you are admitting this fact to yourself.

Over 50 You will have to face up to the fact that you have an eating problem sooner or later, if you have not done so already. Now is the time to do something positive.

Chart 1.2   *Analysis of bingeing*

Part I   Time of eating food that was not on your eating programme

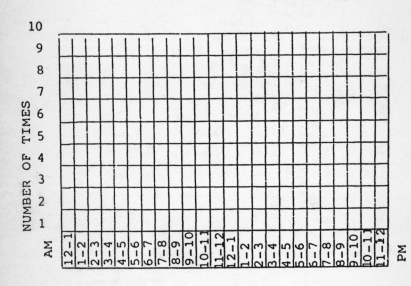

Part II   Place of eating food that was not on your eating programme
Kitchen   _____
Dining room   _____
Living room   _____
Bedroom   _____
Place of entertainment/recreation   _____
At work/school   _____
Canteen   _____
Restaurant/cafe   _____
Pub/night club/disco   _____
Car/bus/train   _____
Walking   _____
Friend/relative's home   _____
Other   _____

Part III   Physical position
Standing   _____
Sitting   _____
Lying down   _____
Walking around   _____

Chart 1.2 *cont.*

Part IV   With whom you ate
      Alone
      Spouse only   ————
      Children only   ————
      Whole family   ————
      Relatives   ————
      Friends   ————
      Acquaintances   ————
      Workmates   ————
      Strangers   ————
      Other   ————

Part V   Associated activity
      Eating only
      Talking   ————
      Reading   ————
      Listening to the radio or records   ————
      Watching television   ————
      At a concert/theatre/cinema   ————
      Cooking   ————
      Clearing table   ————
      Working   ————
      Other   ————

Part VI   Degree of hunger
      0–2 (None to mild)
      3–5 (Mild to moderate)   ————
      6–10 (Moderate to extreme)   ————

Part VII   Circumstances when eating the food not on your eating
      programme
      After drinking alcohol
      Before/after trouble with the family   ————
      Before/after facing a stressful situation   ————
      After being very 'good' about food   ————
      After weighing yourself   ————
      When you are premenstrual   ————
      When pressurised by others to eat   ————
      When others were eating it   ————
      When there was nothing else available in the house   ————

Part VIII   Mood
      Neutral
      Content   ————
      Happy   ————
      Tense   ————
      Depressed   ————

15

Chart 1.2 *cont.*

Angry ———

Irritable ———

Bored ———

Fatigued ———

Rushed ———

Frustrated ———

Restless ———

Slightly drunk ———

Part IX   Day of the week
Friday ——— Saturday ——— Sunday ———
Monday ——— Tuesday ——— Wednesday ——— Thursday ———

Part X   Type of food eaten that was not on your eating programme
Alcohol ———
Sweets ———
Chocolate ———
Cakes ———
Biscuits ———
Pastry ———
Muesli ———
Other breakfast cereals ———
Dried fruits (anything containing it) ———
Puddings ———
Jam/marmalade ———
Ice cream ———
Soft drinks and squashes ———
Sweetened yogurt ———

Part XI   Food permitted on the programme but eaten to excess
Hard cheese ———
Bread ———
Pasta ———
Potatoes ———
Butter/margarine ———
Cream ———
Fruit: apples ———
      bananas ———
      grapes ———
      others ———

CHAPTER TWO

Types of Compulsive Eater

> Proud men in their feasts become fools.
> Latin proverb

There are a number of different types of compulsive eater. You may fit into one type or be a combination of several. Every type has its mild and serious cases.

1.   *The malnourished compulsive eater*   It is essential to have a mixed diet that includes protein, carbohydrates and fats, vitamins and minerals. Without the proper mixture of fuel the body will not function properly. Quality of food is far more important than quantity in keeping healthy.

If you do not know or understand which foods contain protein, which carbohydrates and so on, study the chapter on 'A Plan for Healthy Eating' and take the positive step of buying or borrowing from the library a simple book on the subject. Ignorance is no excuse (although it is surprisingly widespread, even among well-educated people and those in professions such as nursing).

2.   *The hungry compulsive eater*   Not eating enough is probably the main cause of bingeing. It is very difficult, in some cases impossible, for the compulsive eater to come to terms with the fact that if she eats more at normal times she will be less likely to binge. There is a mental block when it comes to taking the plunge to work out a sensible eating plan, but if you know you are not going to binge, you could probably accept a higher weight.

3.   *The angry compulsive eater*   This is a direct expression of

emotion through food. Imagine a couple who have an argument in the middle of a meal. One person, probably the husband, will push his plate away because his anger has completely taken away his appetite. The other one, who has an eating problem, will angrily eat everything on her plate and anything he has left as well.

Later chapters deal with the importance of sorting out the emotional level before the eating problems can be brought under control.

4. *The empty house syndrome* Most compulsive eaters dread being alone in the house because they know it will lead to bingeing. There is the single girl who copes with a diet when she is out at work, but binges when she comes back to a lonely bedsit. Then there is the wife who only binges once a week, the evening when her husband goes out for his regular darts night, leaving her alone.

5. *The bored compulsive eater* Another reason for bingeing is simply for something to do. This is often found in the Sunday binger who is under control during the week with the work routine, but does not have enough interests and hobbies to occupy leisure hours.

6. *The dissatisfied compulsive eater* This is the person who endlessly prowls around in search of something to satisfy her desire to eat. Restless and irritable, she nibbles at this and that but never feels satisfied and the end result is a high-calorie total. Intellectual hunger, frustration with life and the inability to face up to a problem often lie behind this restless prowling. She needs something to use up that restless energy; relaxation and meditation techniques are particularly helpful, but the basic need is to tackle the root cause of dissatisfaction in her life.

7. *The compulsive eater of left-overs* After breakfast is a danger time when it is tempting to finish off everything the children have left on their plates. Good intentions of dieting are broken and you carry on eating for the rest of the day. Children nearly always leave food, so give them smaller portions, then if they are still hungry let them fill up on an apple. That way there is less likely to be any pieces of toast and sausages left over. If you have to take the children to school, dispose of all scraps before you go out so they will not be there to confront you when you

return to an empty house. Older children should clear and wash up their own plates. Another way out is to commit yourself to a busy timetable early in the morning, such as a hair appointment at 9 am, leaving you less time to think about eating.

8.   *The compulsive eater under stress*   These days people have much more leisure time, but many people have a great problem in switching off and relaxing at weekends and during holidays. Compulsive eaters in general tend to be all or nothing people, they are either immaculately groomed or sloppy, their homes are cleaned daily from top to bottom or always dirty and untidy. They put so much of themselves into their work that they find it stressful to be faced with the opportunity of relaxing. They need to learn to meet themselves half way.

9.   *The PMT compulsive eater*   There are many women who only face the urge to binge in the days before their period. If premenstrual tension is the problem, ask your doctor or family planning clinic for help.

10.   *The social drinker*   Without exception alcohol makes people binge. Not only does it increase hunger but it also lessens self-control and lowers the blood sugar level. There are also people who have an allergic reaction to alcohol. A glass of sherry before a meal is intended to stimulate the appetite, and drinking in the evening will give a tendency to eat a lot that night or the next day. A sincere intention to follow a course that will lead to control of eating habits means temporarily giving up alcohol. Once you feel in control you might be able to handle drinking safely, but to begin with it will undermine all the good work you are doing. If you find it impossible to give up drinking, it is worth considering if you have a problem here as well and Alcoholics Anonymous may be able to offer you help.

11.   *The compulsive eater with low blood sugar*   Low blood sugar is often caused by bad eating habits, but it does tend to run in families and some people have less resilience to coping with changes in blood sugar levels than others. Low blood sugar is definitely connected with bingeing. Some people may have had hypoglaecemia diagnosed by their doctor without connecting it with their eating habits.

12.   *The allergic compulsive eater*   Certain foods, in particular things like cereals, refined foods, additives, dried fruit and

alcohol can act as trigger foods as explained more fully in the chapter on allergies and triggers. Some people may be triggered to binge by dairy foods, and oddly enough these often tend to be farmers. Filling in the charts and weekly summaries will expose what foods tend to trigger off a binge for you.

13. *The night-time compulsive eaters* These are the people who go to sleep at night then wake up during the night to eat. In extreme cases there are those who eat in their sleep. The main cause of this is simply hunger. It is common amongst those who starve themselves during the day. Stress and deep-seated psychological problems are another reason along with low blood sugar and food allergies.

14. *The shift-work compulsive eater* In this category fall nurses, a profession with more than its fair share of compulsive eaters. Irregular living patterns that interfere with the body's natural cycles play havoc with eating patterns as well. A sensible programme of well-balanced meals is particularly important. Arrange to eat your main meal when you feel most in need of it, whatever time of the day or night that may be, and that will cut down on the urge to binge on the wrong type of food.

15. *The emotionally drained compulsive eater* Another reason why nurses and other people in caring professions are prone to bingeing is because they are giving something of themselves all the time and often feel they are getting little in return. At the end of the day they feel empty and they need to go home and replenish themselves, but often food is the only replenishment they are able to give themselves.

16. *The vegetarian compulsive eater* At least 50 per cent of women who come to the Maisner Centre with eating problems are vegetarians. A well-balanced vegetarian diet is extremely healthy, but many people do not know what to eat if they give up meat so their diet tends to be a normal one that simply lacks animal products and the essential protein these contain. A vegetarian needs to know what foods should be substituted to give a proper balanced diet or she will begin to suffer from malnutrition – a major cause of bingeing.

CHAPTER THREE

How Much Should You Weigh?

No one is free who is a slave to the body.
Seneca

Most compulsive eaters are concerned about their weight, even though many are not overweight according to weight charts. These charts are usually produced by life insurance companies, based on statistics of the age at which different people die and at what weight, and they also compute average weights of the population. This produces the average weight for each height and build. However these are only a general guide, and it is important not to become obsessive about keeping to any exact weight. The weight graph given here (see Graph 3.1) shows a weight range that you should aim at according to your height and build.

If you believe you should weigh less than the minimum ideal weight given on the chart, you want to be unreasonably thin and should ask yourself why. If you can't think of a sensible answer, you should perhaps consider seeing a therapist, because it is possible that your reasons for wanting to be so thin are caused by a deep-seated psychological disorder.

Many compulsive eaters are under 5 feet 2 inches, and if they are also of very small build they can reasonably expect a low weight. Very small women have to watch their weight more carefully because an extra half stone is a lot for them, where it would make little difference on a tall girl. It is much easier for a small woman to become obsessed with her weight and eating. Two women of the same metabolic rate would need different

21

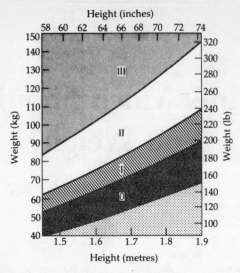

Graph 3.1 *Ideal weights for given heights*

Area O is normal weight; areas I, II and III are different degrees of obesity. Reproduced from *Treat Obesity Seriously* by Dr Garrow, published by Churchill Livingstone.

amounts of calories if they were of different heights, the shorter woman needing less than the taller woman. Some people are just naturally slim, just as some are naturally tall, some naturally dark haired, and no one of these things can be changed; they are due to genetic inheritance.

Why are some people naturally slim? It could be because they have a lot of bone and muscle which uses up more calories than fat even at rest. This could be because they are very active and have tensed muscles even when apparently resting. Some slim people consume very few calories – they prefer salad to pastry or just have small appetites. They may even have problems with digestion or ill-fitting dentures.

Yet some people who are petite, lazy and greedy still stay slim. How can this be? The secret is that they inherited a large number of very active mitochondria. These are tiny power-houses present inside the cells of which the body is composed. These extra mitochondria are especially situated in the brown adipose tissue (B.A.T. or 'brown fat'). If the body is opened up it is possible to see a difference in colour between the two types of fat: storage fat is white; 'brown fat' is actually off-white in colour. If a naturally slim person gets cold the mitochondria switch on to burn fat, changing it to carbon dioxide and water (which are disposed of by the lungs and kidneys). The burning process is not related to any useful work such as walking but the heat produced protects against hypothermia. Naturally fat people (and the elderly) have fewer mitochondria and are more likely to suffer from hypothermia, despite the extra insulation of the mounds of white fat. (Thin elderly people are particularly in danger.)

However, even when they do not *need* to generate heat the naturally slim will do so just by overeating. Any surplus food stimulates the mitochondria to generate useless heat and to waste the surplus food. When the famine comes they will have only a limited reserve, but the fatties can survive off their stores for months (though they will suffer from lack of protein, vitamins and minerals). In a modern society we do not need extra mitochondria to keep warm – we have clothing and central heating. Nor do we need to carry food stores with us – a plastic credit card is more convenient. Overeating is wasteful whether it is changed into heat or stored up for the famine which never comes. Extra food is only justified if used to fuel productive work, to 'pull that barge and lift that bale'.

A system of slimming was marketed which depended on exposure to cold to lose weight. It was based on an experiment on young healthy males – they did not need to lose weight but they lost it. The average slimming club client wouldn't lose an ounce – just the seven pounds charged for the booklet.

Most people find fat repulsive on themselves or anyone else, and you know whether you are carrying too much loose, flabby flesh. It is not weight that counts but the quantity of fat; for example a boxer and an unfit beer drinker may be the same height and weight, but one has a figure to be admired while the other merely has a beer gut.

With a lot of hard work you can change your shape. Exercise is essential for keeping away unsightly bulging flesh, and careful choice of clothes can also flatter your figure. Many people find that when they do lose weight, it does not go from the place they want it to; their bust shrinks, but their thighs remain thick. Many women follow an endless quest for a flat stomach, even though the female body is meant to have a rounded stomach. Through much of history this shape was considered feminine and desirable, and fashion even emphasised the shape of the abdomen. It is only recently that the fashion has changed. If you are extremely overweight, then losing weight will reduce the size of your abdomen, but continuing to diet until your weight is below that shown on the chart will not make your abdomen smaller, although exercise and good posture can help a lot.

Nobody has the perfect figure, everyone has something they are not happy with. Girls with long legs and slim hips complain they have no bust, while those with a good bust grumble about their bulging abdomen. The list of complaints is endless. You have to come to terms with what you are and learn to make the most of it. A sensible diet will bring you to an ideal weight in time and with the help of exercise. If you have a natural tendency to put weight on easily, you just have to accept the fact that you will need to watch your diet for the rest of your life.

From our experience at the Maisner Centre, it appears that most people have a natural weight at which their body seems happy, a weight to which they return when not overeating or dieting. Unfortunately this natural weight is often not the same as the ideal weight quoted on charts and is usually above it. This would suggest that you must either be content at your natural weight or be prepared to always watch the extra pounds to remain at your ideal weight. If you are constantly obsessed and unhappy with your figure, even when you become slim, this could be a case of poor self-esteem. If you do not see yourself capable of being beautiful and attractive, then work is needed on the emotional problems related to your self-image rather than on the shape of your body.

On some days you will feel fatter than on others. This applies especially to women. It has nothing to do with how much you have eaten, but depends on your bodily cycles. Everyone has a

24

variety of natural cycles working within and around them like the seasons of the year. Women have their menstrual cycles; men have times when their beards grow faster than at other times. Everyone has days when they feel more bloated than others. It is a good idea to have a set of clothes that is too big for you to wear on these days; putting on a skirt that feels too tight is asking for trouble. If the compulsive eater wakes in the morning feeling fat, she will eat more that day rather than less.

Why do you want to be slim?

It is part of our western culture to admire a slim figure and the media constantly promote the ideal woman as being pencil slim. Overweight is also associated with bad health and early death because of the epidemic proportions that heart disease has reached. Yet a couple of generations ago people tended to exaggerate their weight because being underweight was associated with the killer disease tuberculosis.

Being able to walk into a shop and buy clothes to fit off the peg is a great joy, but this has more to do with a well-proportioned figure than with a particularly slim one. Those who are size 18 or more suffer agonies trying to buy clothes, and they meet little sympathy from shop assistants, while manufacturers rarely produce fashionable clothes for them.

Being thin and small is also associated with being feminine by those women who wish to be dominated and looked after by men. This is related more to personality than to size. If you want to use the excuse of being thin and pale for getting out of the housework, sex or responsibility in general, this is not a weight problem, nor is making a scene and not eating if someone upsets you. Emotional blackmail by refusing to eat or blaming someone else for your over-eating is an escape back into childhood when as a baby you could use food to attract mother's attention. These are emotional problems and they need to be treated as such. Losing or gaining weight will not cause them to go away. Everyone has to take responsibility for their own bodies.

There are certain jobs which do depend on having an exceptionally slim figure, in particular models and jockeys. Air hostesses are expected to keep within a certain weight limit for their height and build, but this is usually fairly generous according to established weight charts. If your job is causing you serious eating and personality problems, it is really time to consider just how important that job is and if you would not be better off doing something different. If you find it impossible to keep your weight down to the level required for your job without seriously damaging your health, you must face up to the fact you are in the wrong job. Your problem is just the same as that of the hairdresser who has to change her career because she cannot get rid of dermatitis.

On the other hand ask yourself if being ultra-slim is really essential to the job. With jockeys weight is vital, but in modelling or acting there are plenty of examples of those who have made it to the top without being super thin. For example, Hattie Jacques thrived on being outsized, and Dolly Parton definitely has more to offer than a flat-chested girl.

MARY became obsessed about her weight because she sings in a choir which appears on television, and the television cameras have a nasty habit of making everyone look a little bit wider than they actually are. She starved herself so much she ruined her health, and the subsequent bingeing and vomiting began to affect her voice. Eventually she had to realise that her place in the choir depended on her voice, not on her size, and her health was far more important than her figure.

The message when it comes to weight is the same as the one regarding food. Be sensible, be careful but don't become obsessive. Dressmakers may have a standard measurement that is supposed to fit the average person, but the human body is not supposed to be like a manufactured article, every one coming off the production line identical.

Looking good requires a lot more than 'ideal' statistics. Personality is what attracts people far more strongly than looks, so care about your figure as an extension of your personality, not at the expense of it.

CHAPTER FOUR

A Plan for Healthy Eating

He who eats least eats most.
Spanish proverb

There are plenty of books around on healthy eating, it is taught in schools, and magazines and newspapers regularly feature articles on the subject, yet it is surprising how few people actually know what a balanced diet involves, and it is a fact that even fewer keep to one.

Taking an interest in nutrition and making the effort to learn what you should and should not include in a daily diet is a very positive step for the compulsive eater to take. The more you understand your problem, the easier it will be to control your eating. Ignorance is just an excuse for clinging to bad habits; refusing to find out shows a fear of discovering that changes need to be made. So buy or borrow from the library a simple but comprehensive book (see the list in Appendix I at the end of this book). Don't rely on leaflets produced by manufacturers for information as these tend to be slanted towards their own particular product. Ignore all advertisement for manufactured foods; the manufacturers have their interests at heart – not your waistline.

The eating plan

From experience acquired by helping many thousands of people with eating problems at the Maisner Centre, it has become clear that compulsive eaters have special needs when it comes to learning how to get their eating under control. The eating plan recommended here has been tailor-made for those people with eating problems. It has been designed from experience of how compulsive eaters cope with food and is based on a sound knowledge of nutrition. For these reasons, it is likely to be vastly better than the usual daily diet of a binger, but you may wish to show the diet to your doctor and consult him before beginning to follow it, especially if you suffer from any physical disorder for which you are receiving treatment.

The first thing to understand about this eating plan is that it is not a calorie counting diet. A fanatical concern with counting calories is one of the causes of compulsive eating, because it develops an obsession with the details of eating instead of focusing on an overall picture of a balanced diet. To begin with, don't worry about the quantities you are eating, but eat slowly and strictly according to the plan, listening to your own body, so, in time, you will discover exactly what amounts are right for you. In this way good eating habits are developed and become an automatic way of life, even though it might take quite a time to achieve this.

By including 90 grammes of protein and 30 grammes of fibre in your diet each day you can feel confident that you are giving your body enough of these essentials for health, but it is impossible to give an exact guide as to individual needs: an 18-stone man who is 6 feet tall is going to have very different requirements from a woman just 5 feet tall and weighing 8 stone. The whole concept behind the eating plan is to develop a natural understanding of what your own bodily needs are; this is the basic secret of getting eating under control.

Of course, this cannot be achieved overnight. For the first month on the eating plan the important thing is to forget about trying to reduce your weight for the time being and concentrate on getting your eating habits under control. Many compulsive eaters do not realise that by careful choice of food, it is possible to have a balanced diet, eat a good quantity of food and not feel hungry. In fact many panic and feel guilty if they do not feel hungry all the time and they assume they must have been over-eating. By following the eating plan you will be eating well without taking in a great number of calories, so just forget all about calories.

By the end of the first month you should be feeling better, though exactly how long it takes for benefits to be experienced can vary widely from one person to the next. But around this time you should find the craving for sweets and alcohol disappears, you will be feeling less hungry and it will be easier to start exercising regularly. Weight reducing then becomes easier and you should gradually begin to lose weight, although with the increased feeling of well-being that sticking faithfully to the regime brings, you will probably panic less about your weight as other things in life become more important.

Following this eating plan usually has one of two effects. Either you will feel terrific as soon as you start, or you will feel very tired as your body adjusts from a diet of high sugar, starch and caffeine. If you fall into the second group it is because your body is temporarily missing the instant energy effects of these substances, so for the first seven days it is probably advisable to eat more sweet fruit during the day.

Occasionally a compulsive eater wants to put on weight. They need the same nutrients to stay healthy, so should eat the same types of food – just more of them. Being underweight may be due to faulty digestion, stress and tension – the type of nerve problems which can be caused by too much coffee, other stimulants and various forms of poor nutrition. If you are underweight, you can also supplement your basic diet with nuts, soya beans, mayonnaise and the higher calorie green-groceries, such as avocados, olives, jacket potatoes and pulses (plus bananas if they are not a trigger food).

If the eating plan is to be successful, you must stick to the following rules:

The Ten Commandments

1 Eat three meals and at least three snacks every day.
2 Start every day with a protein breakfast.
3 Include 90 grammes of protein in your diet each day.
4 Include 30 grammes of fibre each day.
5 Do not eat any concentrated sugars, such as treacle, honey, white or brown sugar, molasses, or jam.
6 Do not eat breakfast cereals.
7 Any bread, pasta or rice should be whole grain.

8   Do not drink any alcohol.
9   Cut out caffeine (such as coffee, cocoa, tea and cola).
10 Don't be obsessive about your food and enjoy following the
    eating plan.

The reasons for these rules are explained in more detail in the next chapter but in the beginning it is vital to make a commitment to follow them *all* without question. Cheating or changing the rules in any way to suit yourself will limit the success of your programme and you will be the loser. Don't blame the eating plan if it does not work because you are not following it properly. If you find any of these rules impossible to stick to, take a close look at your reasons. Do you really have a valid reason or is it just an elaborate excuse for not facing up to getting your eating under control?

It is not necessary to count calories, but if you are anxious about them you will be pleased to know that for most people the calorie total will be no higher than most reducing diets. This is assuming meat is eaten in affordable quantities, and the extras shown in the last column of the eating plan are few and far between. You are unlikely to be hungry, but never miss a meal or a snack, or think you can lump all your food together in one meal at the end of the day: *when* you eat is as important as *what* you eat in this plan. If necessary, have an extra protein food plus fruit or vegetable snack to avoid getting hungry. Hunger leads to bingeing. Get to know how much your body needs by experience rather than obsessive weighing or calculations. Stick to the correct types of foods and sensible spacing between meals and snacks.

The eating plan is a well-balanced diet that will benefit everyone whether they have an eating problem or not. It can be used as a basis for family meals, but if your family flatly refuse to give up their chips and puddings, accept the fact and cater accordingly. With some ingenuity it should be possible to produce many aspects of the eating plan and keep your family happy without them realising they are 'on a diet'.

If you are following a diet prescribed by your doctor for specific medical reasons other than eating problems you should consult with him before embarking on this diet. If you have any known allergies or know that certain foods cause medical problems, don't eat those foods under any circumstances. There are substitutes in this eating plan.

The first column in the eating plan provides a list of possible foods for one day's balanced diet. Make use of as many of the alternatives as you can; basically, you can eat whatever you like provided it doesn't break any of the 'ten commandments'. Use the protein chart (p. 47) to devise your own eating plan. With a little imagination, it is possible to think up a wide variety of foods to include, so you need never get bored. For example, if you don't like eggs for breakfast, a suitable alternative for 'egg and slice of ham without fat' might be 'a slice of low fat cheese and a tomato', or 'half a tin of tuna (in brine), mixed with half a tin of haricot beans'. Vegetarians will find suitable protein alternatives on the chart too.

The importance of the right diet

Magazines and books bombard us with all sorts of diets to try, but anyone wanting to lose weight should take care to select a diet which is sensible and well balanced. If they also have an eating problem, they must take extra care to find out about the sort of diet that would be beneficial to them. Diets come and go with fashion, but the only really safe and permanent way to lose weight is to reform your eating habits, to take in fewer unnecessary calories while still making sure of adequate nutrition.

Sometimes manufacturers devise 'crash' diets that contain large amounts of their own product, but beware of anything that suggests you live on bananas for a week, or nothing but grapefruit and black coffee. The fact that there are so many thousands of diets around proves that they do not work effectively and people are still continuing to be overweight. The slimming industry is big business these days, shelves are packed with instant slimmers meals, some of which can be used with discretion by those with eating problems, while others should be avoided. For example 'slimming' biscuits are no more helpful to the compulsive eater than ordinary biscuits and are just as likely to lead to bingeing.

		Alternatives	Optional extras and alternatives for people not needing to lose weight
ON RISING	½ Grapefruit or grapefruit juice or small orange or 2 satsumas	Small glass of skimmed milk or ½ carton natural yogurt	Glass of ordinary milk
BREAKFAST	½ grapefruit or unsweetened juice Egg and slice of ham without fat, mushrooms Skimmed milk with decaffeinated coffee	Small bowl of porridge made with water, skimmed milk on top Any alternative protein food,** tomatoes Cup of hot Bovril	Wholemeal bread with peanut butter,* Marmite or margarine (not marmalade, honey or jam)
MID MORNING	Piece of fruit (not banana)	Small glass of unsweetened fruit juice	*Banana
LUNCH	Any fat-free meat, poultry, non-oily fish or shellfish Salad – cucumber, tomato, lettuce, celery, peppers Crispbread with Bovril	Any alternative protein food.** Any fresh salad – including fruit, onions, raw carrots Small slice of wholemeal bread	Extra wholegrain crispbreads or bread. *Nuts (sprinkle on the salad) or include some brown rice or wholemeal pasta or jacket potato
MID AFTERNOON	Small plain yogurt or small glass of skimmed milk (if hungry add bran and fruit)	Triangle of processed cheese and piece of fruit	Camembert or lowfat *cheese with crispbreads
LATE AFTERNOON (if dinner more than 6 hours after lunch)	Hard boiled egg with low calorie coleslaw or tomatoes	Homemade vegetable soup with added bran	Wholegrain crispbread with cottage cheese or *peanut butter
DINNER	Clear soup if desired Meat, poultry, or non-oily fish Greens, carrots, jacket potato Homemade jelly from gelatine and sugar-free fruit or juice	Tomato juice Eggs, cod roe, liver or any other alternative protein food** Any vegetables, including small potato in jacket Skimmed quark-type cheese with fresh fruit	Prawn cocktail Herring, mackerel, tuna in oil, sardines Jacket potato, sweet corn Avocado
MID EVENING (if 2nd late afternoon snack not taken)	Brown wheat crispbread with cottage cheese garnished with salad or fruit	Lettuce leaf or cabbage leaf filled with cottage cheese, tuna or pilchard and salad-type garnish	Small pack of peanuts* (25 grams) or selection of mixed nuts
BEDTIME (if desired)	Small glass of skimmed milk cold or hot with sweetener and vanilla essence	Beverage Triangle of cheese and/or Bovril on crispbread with tomato	Wholemeal bread toasted, spread with Marmite – generous quantity

*Beware if these foods trigger a binge
**See list of alternative protein foods

Alternative protein foods
(Choice based on amount of protein for calories)

Best choice group	Second choice group	Third choice group
Cod, haddock, coley, plaice, whiting	Beef	Corned beef (lean)
(White fish including smoked haddock)	Lamb, Pork, Ham, Heart — Remove all fat	Bacon (grilled and drained)
All types of shellfish (from winkles to lobster and oysters)	Liver, brains	Mince (well-cooked, fat drained)
Fish roe	Sweetbreads	Mackerel/herring (in Summer or Autumn)
Mackerel/herring (in Spring)	Salmon	*Camembert
Pilchards, canned in tomato or brine	Tuna (drain off oil)	*Parmesan
Tuna in brine	Sardines	*Gruyère
Chicken or turkey, no skin	Mackerel/herring (in Winter)	*Emmental
Game – rabbit, grouse, partridge, pheasant	Kippers	*Shape, Cheddar type
Venison	Huss	*Tendale, Cheddar or Cheshire type
Kidney, tripe	†Skimmed milk	†Soya beans
†Cottage cheese	†Low fat plain yogurt	†Soya flour
†Quark-type skimmed cheese (Sainsbury's or Waitrose)	†Eggs	†Tofu (soya bean curd)
†Protoveg, T.V.P. meat substitutes, any brand without added fat		†Pulses, peas and beans
Bovril		†Soya products in general (but read the small print!)
†Marmite yeast extract		*†Nuts – occasionally
†Yeast		

†Suitable for vegetarians
*Beware if these foods trigger off a binge

Starving to lose weight has a very short-lived effect. First you will lose water and glycogen from the stores in the liver, then you will lose water and protein in the form of muscle. You will also lose water associated with salt as starvation is a 'low salt diet'. Of course you will lose some fat at the same time, but it will only be a small part of the weight loss. In one experiment a man lost 10½ pounds in a week on starvation – tests showed it to be 3½ pounds of fat and 7 pounds of water, glycogen and protein.

In another experiment – the ultimate in starvation as no fluid was taken – there was a loss of 9 pounds in 23 hours. (The experiment did not go on for the planned 24 hours – the volunteer became too ill.) Only ½ pound was fat, the other 8½ pounds were all regained by the end of the week on a modest maintenance level diet of 1,700 calories a day. Bingeing will result in an even more horrifying post-starvation weight gain. Fat changes are much slower and can be completely masked by short-term changes. Loss of a quantity of muscle produces a lowered metabolic rate (see Chapter Five) and this makes it continually more difficult to lose weight in the future. Under-eating is the major cause of bingeing, so the right diet must allow enough calories and nutrients each day to keep you satisfied, even if it means weight loss is not as rapid as you might wish. In the long term your weight loss will be much more satisfactory; as can be illustrated by a comparison of two compulsive eaters, Jane and Claire.

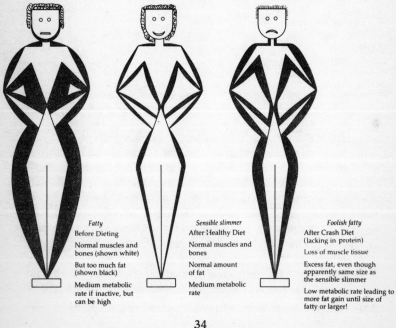

Fatty
Before Dieting

Normal muscles and bones (shown white)

But too much fat (shown black)

Medium metabolic rate if inactive, but can be high

Sensible slimmer
After Healthy Diet

Normal muscles and bones

Normal amount of fat

Medium metabolic rate

Foolish fatty
After Crash Diet
(lacking in protein)

Loss of muscle tissue

Excess fat, even though apparently same size as the sensible slimmer

Low metabolic rate leading to more fat gain until size of fatty or larger!

JANE began to panic because she was due to go off on holiday in eight weeks' time and had set herself the target of losing 10 pounds before she went. But her attempts at starving herself led to uncontrollable binges and by the time she went off on her holiday she was actually 2 pounds heavier than before she had begun her 'diet'.

CLAIRE realised that getting her eating under control was more important than losing her weight, and after eight weeks of carefully following the eating plan to control her eating she was delighted to discover she had also lost 4 pounds. Although she was eating more calories than usual at each meal she was not bingeing, and so her total calorie intake over the period was less.

In Chart 4.1 the diets of the two girls are compared. You can see from this that although at first glance Claire seems to be eating more than Jane, in fact her total intake of food is less.

Chart 4.1 *Comparison of Claire's diet and Jane's diet*

CLAIRE

Monday		Calories
½ pt skimmed milk (daily allowance)		100

Breakfast

1 satsuma	approx.	30
1 boiled egg (size one)		95
¾ oz wholemeal bread		50

Snack

1 Ryvita crispbread		25
1 cheese triangle		40
1 tomato		10

Lunch

3½ oz tinned tuna fish in brine		110
Large green salad	approx.	20
½ banana	approx.	50
5 oz carton natural low fat yogurt		75

Snack

1 oz boiled lean ham		60
1 apple	approx.	50

Dinner

Tin game consomme		50
3 oz grilled liver		150
Greens	approx.	12
½ jacket potato without butter	approx.	50

Evening Snack

¾ oz wholemeal bread		50
1 oz tinned sardines in tomato sauce		52
		1,079

JANE

Monday	Calories
5 oz carton of natural low fat yogurt with ½ oz natural bran	104
5 oz tinned baked beans with tomato sauce	100
1 fruit gum	5
3½ oz cucumber	10
Fresh lemon drink – no sugar	2
2 oz raw carrot	13
Fresh lemon drink – no sugar	2
	236

CLAIRE

Tuesday		Calories
½ pt skimmed milk (daily allowance)		100

Breakfast

4 oz smoked haddock with butter		145
1 grilled tomato		10
½ grapefruit	approx.	15

Snack

2 oz cottage cheese	54
¾ oz wholemeal bread	50

Lunch

2 oz chicken breast, roast without skin		84
Green salad	approx.	20

Snack

½ oz Brie cheese		44
1 orange	approx.	70

Dinner

Slice melon	approx.	25
4 oz lean roast lamb		288
3½ oz cabbage, boiled		14
4 oz strawberries		28

Evening snack

1 Ryvita crispbread	25
1 oz tinned tuna in brine	27
1 tomato	10
	1,009

JANE

Tuesday	Calories
Black cherry yogurt	175
1 oz natural bran	29
5 fruit gums	25
4½ oz raw mushrooms	17
1 fruit gum	5
Fresh lemon drink – no sugar	2
10 oz cabbage, boiled	40
	293

CLAIRE

Wednesday		Calories
½ pt skimmed milk (daily allowance)		100

Breakfast
2 oz canned pears		39
1 boiled egg		95
1½ oz wholemeal bread		100

Snack
2 oz cottage cheese		54
1 Ryvita crispbread		25
1 orange	approx.	70

Lunch
| 2 oz lean boiled ham | | 120 |
| Large green salad | approx. | 25 |

Snack
| 1 cheese triangle | | 40 |
| 2 tomatoes | | 20 |

Dinner
Pheasant consomme		50
2 cod steaks, grilled		160
6 oz cauliflower, boiled		18
4 oz carrots, boiled		20
4 oz blackberries, stewed without sugar		28

Evening Snack
| 5 oz carton natural low fat yogurt | | 75 |
| | | **1,039** |

JANE

Wednesday	Calories
Swiss roll, jam and vanilla, 6 oz	600
5 oz carton single cream	300
6 slices bread, butter and jam (large slices and portions) approx.	1,400
Tin of rice pudding, 15½ oz	490
1 can custard	425
20 chocolate triangles	1,000
2 doughnuts	380
1 Mars bar	270
1 Yorkie milk chocolate bar	325
	5,190

CLAIRE

Thursday		Calories
½ pt skimmed milk (daily allowance)		100

Breakfast

½ grapefruit	approx.	15
1 boiled egg (size one)		95
¾ oz wholemeal bread		50

Snack

1 oz lean boiled ham		60
1 satsuma	approx.	30

Lunch

3 oz tinned crab		120
Large green salad	approx.	30
1 peach	approx.	50

Snack

½ oz Brie cheese		44
2 sticks celery		8

Dinner

Slice melon	approx.	25
4 oz lean roast pork, no fat		212
4 oz broccoli, boiled		20
½ jacket potato without butter	approx.	50
4 oz fresh pineapple		52
3 tablespoons yogurt	approx.	30

Evening Snack

1 oz tinned tuna fish in brine		50
1 Ryvita crispbread		25
		1,066

JANE

Thursday	Calories
5 oz carton of natural low fat yogurt with ½ oz natural bran	104
2 Ryvita crispbreads	50
10 mls Marmite (approx. 2 level teaspoons)	20
1 oz watercress	4
10 fruit gums	50
Fresh lemon drink – no sugar	2
1 fruit gum	5
10 oz cabbage, boiled	40
Fresh lemon drink – no sugar	2
2 fruit gums	10
	287

CLAIRE

Friday		Calories
½ pt skimmed milk (daily allowance)		100

Breakfast

2 oz canned pilchards		70
1½ oz wholemeal bread		100
1 tomato		10

Snack

Triangle cheese		40
1 Ryvita crispbread		25
1 tomato		10

Lunch

4 oz prawns		120
Large green salad	approx.	25
1 apple	approx.	50

Snack

5 oz carton natural low fat yogurt		75

Dinner

Bird's Eye liver with onion		190
½ jacket potato without butter	approx.	50
3 oz runner beans, boiled		21
2 oz strawberries and 1 oz grapefruit		20

Evening Snack

1 oz Cheddar cheese		120
1 Ryvita crispbread		25
		1,051

JANE

Friday		Calories
5 oz carton of natural low fat yogurt with ½ oz natural bran		104
10 fruit gums		50
Fresh lemon drink – no sugar		2
10 oz cauliflower, boiled		30
16 fl. oz (approx. 4 glasses) sweet white wine		400
4 oz muesli with 1 pt milk		770
2 peanut butter and banana sandwiches	approx.	1,040
Large portion fish and chips (bought from local shop)	approx.	1,100
2 oz tomato ketchup		60
½ pt lager		120
20 chocolate triangles		1,000
		4,676

A Plan for Healthy Eating

CLAIRE

Saturday		Calories
½ pt skimmed milk (daily allowance)		100

Breakfast

1 boiled egg (size one)		95
¾ oz wholemeal bread		50
1 tangerine	approx.	30

Snack

1½ oz tinned crab		60
1 tomato		10

Lunch

2 oz roast chicken, breast without the skin		84
Green salad	approx.	25
4 oz canned pears		78

Snack

2 oz cottage cheese		54
1 apple	approx.	50

Dinner

Bird's Eye cod in parsley sauce		175
½ jacket potato without butter	approx.	50
3 oz runner beans, boiled		21
Green salad	approx.	25
2 oz strawberries and 1 oz grapefruit		20

Evening Snack (taken in the pub)

2 oz peanuts		336
1 'slimline' shandy		15
		1,278

JANE

Saturday	Calories
5 oz carton of natural low fat yogurt with ½ oz natural bran	104
10 fruit gums	50
2 Ryvita crispbreads	50
10 mls Marmite (approx. 2 level teaspoons)	20
1 oz cucumber	3
Fresh lemon drink – no sugar	2
11 oz cauliflower, boiled	33
1 fruit gum	5
	267

The Food Trap

CLAIRE				JANE	
Sunday			**Calories**	**Sunday**	**Calories**
½ pt skimmed milk (daily allowance)			100	5 oz carton of natural low fat yogurt	
				with ½ oz natural bran	104
Breakfast				2 Ryvita crispbreads	50
1 boiled egg (size one)			95	10 mls Marmite (approx. 2 level	
1½ oz wholemeal bread			100	teaspoons)	20
½ pt skimmed milk			100	1 oz cucumber	3
				Fresh lemon drink – no sugar	2
Snack				1 fruit gum	5
1 apple		approx.	40	8 oz cabbage, boiled	32
1 oz lean boiled ham			60	Fresh lemon drink – no sugar	2
				3½ oz cucumber	10
Lunch					
4 oz cottage cheese			108		
Large green salad		approx.	30		
1 orange		approx.	50		
Snack					
½ oz Cheddar cheese			60		
1 tomato			10		
Dinner					
4 oz lean roast beef			220		
3 oz cauliflower, boiled			9		
2 oz carrots, boiled			10		
4 oz brussels sprouts, boiled			20		
3 tablespoons natural low fat					
yogurt		approx.	30		
Evening Snack					
1 oz tinned sardines in tomato sauce			52		
Tomato and cucumber					
salad		approx.	25		
			1,119		**228**
Week's total calorie intake			**7,641**	**Week's total calorie intake**	**11,177**

CHAPTER FIVE

The Ten Commandments Explained

Law alone can give us freedom.
Goethe

It is now time to explain in greater detail why the list of rules called the Ten Commandments has been imposed, and why it is so vitally important to follow the rules if your eating is to be brought under control.

1. Eat three meals and at least three snacks every day

Little and often is the golden rule when it comes to controlling eating habits. That does not mean life should be one long nibble, but regular small protein meals through the day will cut out the urge to binge from hunger or pick between meals. Bulimics in particular should try to have at least six small meals a day because their stomachs just cannot cope with the feeling of being full. A lot of compulsive eaters find they cannot go for more than four or five hours without eating or they begin to feel unpleasant side effects. The level of sugar in the blood has a very important influence, not only on how you feel physically but also on your moods, so keeping the blood sugar level steady will make you feel more in control than if it is allowed to climb and drop steeply. The best way to maintain a good blood sugar level is to eat many small meals and snacks during the day, as recommended in the eating plan. These snacks should contain protein and carbohydrate. For example, a quick easy snack would be a glass of skimmed milk with a small piece of fruit.

A good average blood sugar level is approximately 90 to 95 milligrammes of sugar in 100 cc of blood for a person who has not eaten for 12 hours. If this is the level on waking in the morning, energy will still be at a reasonable level, but without more food at breakfast time the supply of blood sugar will be used up and energy levels will drop. When the level of sugar in the blood starts to fall, hunger is experienced, together with tiredness and a general feeling of low energy, and as it continues to drop, sugar cravings or a panicky-type of hunger begins. Fatigue turns to exhaustion as the level continues to drop, headaches and weakness often occur, and irritability and depression grow. In extreme cases, this may result in giddiness or even fainting.

It is easy to see from this why starvation or unsuitable diets can easily lead to headaches, depression and bingeing. If breakfast is nothing more than black coffee, by mid-morning the sugar craving can build up, leading to a mid-morning binge of cakes, biscuits, doughnuts or cereals. However, if a good breakfast is eaten, including protein and some wholegrain carbohydrate, the blood sugar level stays about normal throughout the morning, a level at which one would feel well. The beneficial effects of the kind of breakfast recommended by the eating plan can last for as long as six hours. One of the worst breakfasts, on the other hand, is refined breakfast cereals with sugar which cause the production of excess insulin followed by lowering of the blood sugar – below the fasting level.

Studies have shown that summer heat decreases the appetite for protein and increases the craving for sugar-filled iced drinks and ice cream. People tend to eat salads rather than more substantial protein meals, and there is a likelihood of the compulsive eater suffering from hot weather fatigue, together with summer ice cream binges. When hot and thirsty, try to stick to sugar-free drinks or just plain water or ice cubes.

Chart 5.1   *Effect of two types of breakfast on blood sugar levels*

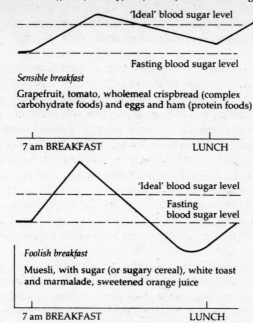

'Ideal' blood sugar level

Fasting blood sugar level

Sensible breakfast

Grapefruit, tomato, wholemeal crispbread (complex carbohydrate foods) and **eggs** and **ham** (protein foods)

7 am BREAKFAST   LUNCH

'Ideal' blood sugar level

Fasting blood sugar level

Foolish breakfast

Muesli, with **sugar** (or **sugary** cereal), white toast and marmalade, **sweetened** orange juice

7 am BREAKFAST   LUNCH

2.   Start every day with a protein breakfast

A common complaint among those with eating problems is 'I can't eat breakfast in the morning.' The reason for this is often poor eating habits, over-eating the night before, or a disorganised life-style that does not leave enough time for a proper breakfast. Following the eating plan conscientiously means making quite a few adjustments to your life, and that might include getting up a bit earlier so you can eat a proper breakfast and making sure you have something handy for your mid-morning snack. How long does it take you to open a tub of cottage cheese? A couple of hard-boiled eggs cooked the night before are a quick and handy basis of a meal or snack. 'I can't eat eggs for breakfast' is no excuse; there are plenty of other protein foods apart from the traditional breakfast – how about a slice of yesterday's roast?

45

One real problem the compulsive eater often faces is 'If I eat breakfast in the morning, I can't stop eating all day.' The usual reason for this is that the wrong kinds of food are being eaten; only eat those items specified on the eating plan, and keep well away from the danger foods such as sugary cereals, and in particular, muesli, with its cereal, sugar and dried fruit. Decide you have just enough time to enjoy a tin of tuna or a piece of chicken, and then make sure you are committed to getting out of the kitchen so there is no time to think about eating anything else. If you don't have a bus to catch or children to take to school, make an early appointment at the hairdressers or arrange to meet a friend; otherwise just get out of the kitchen and start getting busy in another part of the house.

Don't be tempted to believe 'I eat enough protein in the evening, I don't need it at breakfast as well.' The eating plan specifies that protein intake should be spread throughout the day; if it is eaten only at night it can cause drowsiness, and fatigue can be hidden by alcohol and coffee taken at the same meal. If you have been punishing your blood sugar level for quite some time, letting it fall unnaturally low, then send it rocketing with sugary binges, it may take a while for the situation to level itself out. A period of following the eating plan should help to correct sugar and fluid imbalance, but if you think the problem is not going away you should consult your doctor. Erratic blood sugar level leads to stress and subsequent loss of potassium and retention of sodium, which affects the fluid balance of the tissues, and leads to waterlogging or oedema.

3. Include 90 grammes of protein in your diet each day

Protein is essential for the repair and replacement of body tissue. It is used in the production of hair, skin, nails and blood, as well as hormones, digestive juices, mucus and phlegm. If this building material is not supplied by food, it is 'borrowed' from muscle, leading to flabbiness. Metabolic rate (the number of calories used up each day) is related to the amount of bone and muscle in the body, which is why a 6 feet muscle-man can eat more than a 5 feet elderly lady without getting fat. Lowered metabolic rate means fewer calories are used so more is stored as fat.

Foolish fatties often discard protein from their diets, using a crash diet as a fast way to lose weight, but it is muscle not fat they are losing and this leads to a rebound weight gain later on.

High protein diets also satisfy hunger better; for example, a 7 oz steak is a feast, while a 'meal' of slimming biscuits has many calories and only gives an eighth of the protein and little satisfaction.

The most successful sources of protein are fish, shellfish, the lean of meat and poultry, eggs and the skimmed part of milk. Even vegetarians can get plenty from the last two – including skimmed milk cheese and low fat yogurts for variety (see Chart 5.2).

Chart 5.2 *Amounts of protein in different foods*

	Cals per 100 gms (3½ oz)	Protein per 100 gms (3½ oz)
MEAT		
Bacon		
lean, average, raw	147	20.2
gammon rashers, lean, grilled	172	31.4
middle rashers, lean and fat, grilled	416	24.9
Beef		
lean, average, raw	123	20.3
brisket, boiled, lean and fat	326	27.6
mince, stewed	229	23.1
stewing steak, stewed, lean and fat	223	30.9
topside roast, lean and fat	214	26.6
Lamb		
lean, average, raw	162	20.8
chops, loin grilled, lean and fat	355	23.5
leg, roast, lean and fat	266	26.1
breast, roast, lean only	252	25.6
shoulder, roast, lean and fat	316	19.9
Pork		
lean, average, raw	147	20.7
chops, grilled, lean and fat	332	28.5
leg, roast, lean only	185	30.7

	Cals per 100 gms (3½ oz)	Protein per 100 gms (3½ oz)
Veal		
fillet, raw	109	21.1
roast	230	31.6
Chicken (turkey, slightly less on cals and protein)		
raw, meat only	121	20.5
boiled, meat only	183	29.2
roast, meat only	148	24.8
leg, quarter (weighed with bone)	92	15.4
Offal		
heart, stewed (ox)	179	31.4
kidney, stewed (pig)	153	24.4
kidney, lamb, raw	90	16.5
liver, lamb, raw	179	20.1
liver, ox, stewed	198	30.5
oxtail, stewed	243	30.5
Meat products		
corned beef	217	26.9
sausage, pork, grilled	265	13.0
FISH		
Cod		
grilled	95	20.4
poached	94	20.9
Haddock		
steamed	98	22.8
smoked, steamed	101	23.3
Herring		
raw	234	16.8
grilled	199	20.4
Sardines in oil	289	22.8
Tuna in oil	289	22.8
Trout – brown, steamed	135	23.5
Shellfish		
crab, boiled	127	20.1
prawns, boiled	107	22.6
mussels, boiled	87	17.2
NON-ANIMAL PROTEIN FOOD		
* (by Granose Foods Ltd)		
* Soya bean pate	132	10.8
* T.V.P. Beef flavour	250	51.5
Sweet and sour flavour	250	51.5

	Cals per 100 gms (3½ oz)	Protein per 100 gms (3½ oz)
Chicken flavour	227	46.0
* Bologna	167	20.1
* Sausalatas	137	11.0
* Nut Brawn	212	8.3
* Dinner Balls	225	14.0
* Liquid Soya Milk	51	3.6
Soya flour, full fat	447	36.8
Soya flour, low fat	352	45.3

MILK & MILK PRODUCTS
Milk (cows)

fresh, whole	65	3.3
fresh, skimmed	33	3.4
Butter – salted	740	0.4

Cream

single	212	2.4
double	447	1.5
whipping	332	1.9

Cheese

Camembert type	300	22.8
Cheddar type	406	26.0
Edam type	304	24.4
Cottage cheese	96	13.6
Cheese spread	183	18.3

Yoghurt (low fat)

Natural	52	5.0

Eggs

whole, raw	147	12.3

CEREALS
Grains, etc.

barley, boiled	120	2.7
rice, boiled	123	2.2
spaghetti, boiled	117	4.2
macaroni, boiled	117	4.3
semolina (raw)	350	10.7

Bread

wholemeal	216	8.8
brown	223	8.9

Breakfast cereal

Shredded Wheat	324	10.6
cooked porridge	44	1.4

	Cals per 100 gms (3½ oz)	Protein per 100 gms (3½ oz)
VEGETABLES		
Green mung beans	231	22.0
Red kidney beans	272	22.1
Butter beans, boiled	95	7.1
Haricot beans, boiled	93	6.6
Lentils, split, boiled	99	7.6
Peas, fresh boiled	52	5.0
Peas, dried raw	286	21.6
Sweetcorn, boiled	123	4.1
Potatoes (old) boiled	80	1.4
Potatoes (old) baked	85	2.1
Potatoes (old) chips	253	3.8
FRUIT		
Avocado pears	223	4.2

Protein is vital to a healthy diet, yet many compulsive eaters do not include nearly enough of it, either because they do not know what protein is and how important it is, or because they think it is fattening. In fact, protein is very useful in helping to get eating under control, because its very complex structure means it is digested slowly, and so helps to keep the blood sugar at a steady level. Energy is released slowly and hunger remains satisfied for longer. A well-nourished body is less likely to experience food cravings and the panic and fear associated with starving and bingeing, so it is extremely important to include protein with every meal.

Vegetarians need just as much protein in their diet as anyone else, but often this is lacking because animal products have been cut out of the diet and not replaced by suitable alternatives. Some eat extra cheese, which, in many cases, can be a binge food, but a major cause of bingeing among vegetarians is the body crying out for protein. It is important to understand what combinations of foods give complete proteins (see Chart 5.3), and consider meals that include a drink of skimmed milk with a pulse dish or a serving of yogurt on fruit. Brown rice is a source of protein, but it would be necessary to eat nearly 3,500 calories' worth of rice to get sufficient protein for daily needs if that were the only source, and few people concerned about eating would plan to consume that many calories a day.

If vegetarian eating is based on a dislike of cruelty to animals, why not consider keeping your own free-range chickens, or find someone else who does and buy your eggs from them? Similarly, drink goat's milk from a family pet where there is no suggestion of any kind of cruelty involved. Vegans are the most difficult compulsive eaters to get on to a well-balanced diet, and yet when they binge they are usually not so fussy about what they are eating. For example, a vegan might refuse to take milk in a planned meal, but binge on milk chocolate.

Also because vegans eat nothing of an animal origin, they can easily go short of protein (and also of Vitamin B12, Vitamin D, iron and calcium). The protein in non-animal foods is an incomplete mixture of the amino acids which combine to make human proteins. Vegans need to combine their proteins to improve the quality of the total mixture.

Chart 5.3   *The following combinations of foods will give complete proteins*

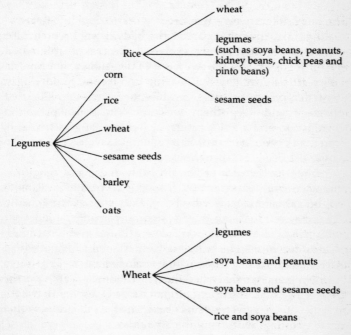

In addition, vegans have the problem that few of the foods shown in Chart 5.3 contain enough protein to get the high level needed without taking in an excess of calories. Best buys for quantity of protein in relation to calories are leaves (cabbage, etc), stems (celery, rhubarb, fennel, asparagus) and flowers (cauliflower, broccoli), but as these are so bulky they need supplementing with pulses (peas and all types of beans, including soya beans) and nuts (but beware of the high calorie content). Wheat, rice, barley and oats are low in protein. To get 90 grammes of pure protein from wholemeal bread, a vegan needs 2,210 calories! No wonder vegans have eating problems. If you are a committed vegan, it is advisable to seek personal advice from a nutritionist to sort out the problems of all the nutrients you could be going short of.

4. Include 30 grammes of fibre each day

The body's digestive system needs work to do if it is to remain healthy. Like any other part of the body it will become flabby and inefficient if it is not exercised. Processed, refined and instant foods take all the work out of digestion and are quickly passed through the system leaving you feeling hungry again. Plenty of fresh fruit and vegetables means fibre to fill out the intestines and keep them working, while also preventing constipation and a quick return of hunger pangs after eating. Bran is a very good form of fibre; adding it to soups or sprinkling it over salads is very beneficial.

Refined carbohydrates are probably the major binge food among compulsive eaters. Such food is so readily available, so easy to eat, and usually very tasty. Even those without eating problems are not doing their system any good by indulging in foods like cakes, biscuits, refined cereals and instant puddings, because the human body was never designed to assimilate and exist on such foods. Those who live alone have no excuse at all for buying such items, while those with families often say they are buying them for the children. In rare cases where children have never been given sweets or biscuits they do not miss them and are content with fruit or nutritious snacks offered in their

Chart 5.4 *Foods high in fibre*

g of fibre per 100 g		g of fibre per 100 g	
Almonds (shelled)	14.3	Lentils, raw	11.7
Barcelona nuts (shelled)	10.3	Loganberries, raw	6.2
Blackberries, raw	7.3	Passion fruit, raw	15.9
Bran wheat	44.0	Peas, fresh, raw	5.2
Bread, wholemeal	8.5	Peanuts, fresh (shelled)	8.1
Butter, raw	21.6	Puffed Wheat	15.4
Cabbage, red, raw	3.4	Raspberries, raw	7.4
Chestnuts (shelled)	6.8	Shredded Wheat	12.3
Coconut, fresh	13.6	Soya flour, full-fat	11.9
Currants, black, raw	8.7	Spinach, boiled	6.3
Damsons, raw	4.1	Sweetcorn, on-the-cob, boiled	4.7
Haricot beans, raw	25.4	Sweetcorn, canned kernels	5.7
Haricot beans, boiled	7.4	Walnuts (shelled)	5.2

place. Never buy more sweets or biscuits than are necessary – just sufficient for other members of the family so there will be nothing left for you to binge on.

Convenience foods are a great cause of compulsive eating because they are so quick and easy. They also usually contain a lot of sugar and additives which can trigger off a binge – experience shows that raw cake mixes, for example, are a great source of bingeing. Nobody knows the true extent of the effect of all the additives that are used in processing and preserving foods, although research has connected hyperactivity and anti-social behaviour in children with an adverse reaction to additives.

The eating plan recommended here excludes refined carbo-hydrates and processed foods and includes a reasonable amount of fibre each day, so after following the plan for a while you should find not only a change in your eating habits, but also an increased sense of general well-being. Increasing the amount of fibre in your diet should in time overcome any problems with constipation, but do not become too obsessed with worrying about bowel movements. Not everyone has a bowel movement every day and if you have not been eating enough you are not likely to. This is no reason for reaching for more laxatives too quickly, but if you have got into the habit of taking a large number of laxatives regularly, it is advisable that you consult your doctor before suddenly deciding to cut them out completely.

5. Do not eat any concentrated sugars

Refined sugar and chocolate are two items that the human race lived without for thousands of years and could well do without today, but the sweet manufacturers continue to push the myth that sugar gives you energy, helps you 'work, rest and play'. Energy, in nutrition terms, means calories and calories means fat. 3,500 calories of energy means 1 pound of bulging blubber. It could mean the 'energy' or fuel to walk from London to Brighton, but only if you have the vitality. A 20 stone woman has at least 10 stone of surplus energy (about half a million calories), but she does not have the vitality to use those calories; they just stay there making her feel tired and probably depressed. Sugar only gives a temporary lift, while the vitality to get you through the day comes from a balance of foods containing protein with plant foods containing fibre and the intricate blending of minute amounts of vitamins and minerals obtained from a varied selection of these foods.

The body only needs a small quantity of sugar which can be obtained from any vegetables or fruits. No one needs to eat refined sugar (whether sucrose, glucose, or any other type), nor do they need honey which is 80 per cent sugar. Fructose (fruit sugar) is tied up inside the cells of plants and is only released slowly as the cells are digested in the gut. Also the quantities are far less than taken in a refined sugar. There is as much sugar in a glass of lemonade as in two apples, but it is drunk and absorbed into the bloodstream in a fraction of the time taken to eat the apples. Take the same amount of sugar in the form of celery and you can eat over 4 pounds which will take all day to get into your bloodstream – or possibly a week to eat!

6. Do not eat breakfast cereals

As Chart 5.6 shows, nearly all breakfast cereals contain a lot of

Chart 5.5   *Foods containing surprisingly large amounts of 'hidden' sugar*

Item	Percentage sugar
Biscuits, digestive	16½
Chutney, sweet mango	over 60
tomato	50.1
Coffee essence	53.8
Dates	63.9
Dried soups, as served	
chicken	10
tomato	36
Jams, sugar-free	over 60
	(mostly fructose)
Lime cordial, undiluted	24.8
Mincemeat	62.1
Ovaltine	73
Peppermints	102.2
Prunes, dried	40.3
Raisins	64.4
Wheatgerm	16

Figures taken from: McCance and Widdowson's *The Composition of Foods* H.M.S.O.
Publications

Chart 5.6   *The hidden sugar content of some breakfast cereals*

Product	Percentage of sugar
Cocoa Krispies	43.0
Sugar Frosted Flakes	41.0
Frosted Rice	37.0
Cocoa Puffs	33.3
Raisin Bran	29.0
Frosted Mini-Wheats	26.0
100% Bran	21.0
All-Bran	19.0
Grape-Nuts Flakes	13.3
40% Bran Flakes	13.0
Rice Krispies	7.8
Grape-Nuts	7.0
Special K	5.4
Corn Flakes	5.3
Shredded Wheat	0.6
Puffed Wheat	0.5
Puffed Rice	0.1

hidden sugar, and although some doctors believe bulimics should eat cereals, experience with compulsive eaters at the Maisner Centre has found they do much better without them. It is very important to have a protein breakfast each day, as has been explained, and so there should be no need for cereals. If you feel particularly hungry or need a higher than usual amount of calories each day (for example, very tall people or manual workers), a cereal without any hidden sugar can be included, such as natural porridge, provided it is not a trigger food. A better alternative would probably be bran, unsweetened fruit juice and yogurt.

7.   Any bread, pasta or rice should be whole grain

If you are of small height and build and your food requirements are minimal, it is better not to include these foods too often in your diet. However most people can eat these foods in moderation while following the eating plan, so it is important that they should provide as high a percentage of nourishment as possible. For this reason, wholemeal bread, wholewheat pasta and unpolished brown rice should replace the refined equivalents as they give fibre and extra vitamins and nutrients to the diet. Potatoes, if eaten, should be baked in their jackets or scrubbed well and boiled in their skins as much of the vitamin content is found just below the skin surface and is removed by peeling. The skin also provides valuable fibre.

Many compulsive eaters tolerate bread very badly, it acts as a trigger that sets them bingeing. If this applies to you leave bread well alone, until you can cope with it.

8.   Do not drink any alcohol

This is a very important rule and should be obeyed absolutely for the first few weeks of the eating plan. If you find it impossible to give up alcohol, consider carefully how much of a hold it has on your life; should you be seeking trained help with your drinking problem as well as sorting out your eating problems? Many people with eating problems also have a problem with drink because both are closely connected with blood sugar levels, so alcohol should be avoided for the same reasons as sweets and sugary foods.

Alcohol also lowers the level of self-control, so it is easier to binge when under the influence of drink. Only when eating is under control and good eating habits are being established might it be safe to begin introducing alcohol again. But in the beginning the only way to handle alcohol is to exclude it completely.

Many compulsive eaters make the excuse that others expect them to drink, that alcohol is 'forced' on them if they go out socially. This is a reflection of the typical inability of most compulsive eaters to assert themselves and say no. All it takes is a firm but polite refusal a few times – say no and *mean* it. Your friends will soon take your attitude for granted. If you were a person who did not like the taste of alcohol, or did not drink for religious or medical reasons, others would accept your refusal without question. Your reason for not drinking is just as valid: alcohol aggravates your eating problems and you choose not to drink because you want to get your eating under control. Alcohol is also very fattening, of course. Don't feel resentful or deprived because you are not allowed alcohol. Concentrate instead on how successfully you are following your eating plan and working towards better eating habits and a better future. Congratulate yourself for tackling this aspect of it so well and enjoy your glass of unsweetened orange juice or tomato juice.

9. Cut out caffeine

As little as three or four cups of coffee a day can make a person psychologically and physically dependent on caffeine, and once hooked, cutting out coffee can lead to withdrawal symptoms such as headaches, drowsiness, lethargy, irritability, panic, inability to work, severe depression, jitters and extreme drowsiness. These symptoms usually appear 12 to 16 hours after the last dose of caffeine, and if you decide to give up coffee abruptly the chances are that you will feel really bad for about four days.

If you are in the habit of drinking a lot of coffee at work you may have noticed blinding headaches at the weekend when your coffee consumption drops. Alternatively, if you drink more coffee at weekends, you may feel bad on a Monday. Cutting out caffeine should remedy such unexplained headaches if they are coffee connected. However, do be prepared for initial ill-effects if you suddenly cut off a high level of coffee drinking. If possible pick a time when you do not have to go to work, undertake any important jobs, or have the children around you all day.

Caffeine is not just found in coffee, but also in such drinks as tea, cocoa and cola, so start reading labels on products you buy and if they do not state the product is caffeine-free, do not buy it. One popular herbal tea, which is described as an ideal morning tea, has twice the amount of caffeine in it as a regular cup of tea, so a useful project would be to discover just which drinks do and do not contain caffeine. Caffeine has an effect similar to sugar, although its action is not so immediate. It stimulates the adrenal glands to increase the blood sugar level, with a subsequent release of insulin to balance the sugar increase. For this reason caffeine can act as a temporary stimulant to keep one awake, but like any other drug caffeine can be addictive. It is often drunk in vast quantities by people with eating problems and weight problems as they believe it has 'no calories' and also that it reduces the appetite.

Chart 5.7 *Caffeine content of typical foods*

Food	Caffeine content
Chocolate bar	160 mg per 8 oz (225 g)
Aspirin-based tablets	15–30 mg each
Coffee	100–150 mg per cupful
Tea	60–75 mg per cupful
Cola drinks	40–60 mg per cupful

It is true that caffeine can raise the basal metabolic rate and thus increase the number of calories the body burns. However, at the same time, it triggers the release of insulin which causes blood sugar to drop producing feelings of hunger and sugar cravings. Coffee is also a diuretic, and drinking vast amounts of coffee often causes an excessive thirst. Because many compulsive eaters do not know the difference between thirst and hunger this again can lead to eating.

It is also believed that people who drink a lot of coffee or beverages containing caffeine tend to be more depressed than other people, although it is not known which comes first, the depression or the high caffeine consumption.

Many people believe they can give up coffee drinking easily, but soon discover it is far more difficult than they anticipated. Signs of coffee addiction are:

1   You show no signs of agitation or other side effects, despite drinking endless cups of coffee.
2   When you give up coffee drinking you begin to experience drowsiness, headaches, trembling, palpitation, panic, restlessness, depression and other side effects.
3   When you are deprived of coffee, you develop a terrible craving for it.

Before embarking on the eating plan it is important to kick the caffeine habit. There are two ways of doing this. If the caffeine intake has not been too high, just cut caffeine out completely and live with the effects of withdrawal for a few days until the symptoms disappear. However if caffeine intake has been very high, it is better to decrease the amount of caffeine slowly. For the heavy coffee drinker, the easiest way to do this is to mix a jar of decaffeinated coffee with ordinary coffee, first of all half and half then in the ratio 2-to-1, 3-to-1 and so on until it becomes completely decaffeinated.

Herbal teas are a good substitute, although they may taste strange at first. Once you get used to them there is a wide variety of flavours to try out. Other alternatives are such drinks as Barleycup; in fact any of the grain-based beverages which you will find on sale in health food stores and some chemists are fine provided you are not allergic to wheat, barley, rye, chicory or beets which they contain. Don't forget that plain water is also a very good drink. If your tap water tastes unpalatable, buy bottled water or get yourself an inexpensive water purifying jug.

As with alcohol, giving up coffee while you are following the eating plan does not necessarily mean you can never drink another cup of coffee again. In time, once your eating is under control, you will probably be able to introduce it again in moderation, but by then you may well find you have lost the desire for it.

10. Enjoy following the eating plan

In some ways this is the most important rule of all, because the attitude with which you tackle the eating plan will determine whether or not you ultimately succeed in getting your eating under control. If you feel you are punishing yourself by placing restrictions on your former eating habits, or feel deprived and ill-used because you are forbidden your favourite food and drink, you will become resentful, bad-tempered and probably abandon the eating plan at the earliest opportunity.

See the eating plan as an exciting challenge, an opportunity for you to really get to grips with your problem and succeed, leading to a much brighter and happier future and a widening of your horizons in years ahead. Of course it is not easy, but think of the pride and satisfaction you will feel when you can look back and realise you have achieved something truly worthwhile.

When following the eating plan, be strict with yourself and don't let bad habits creep back in. At the same time have a realistic approach to your eating and always keep a sense of proportion. For instance, much has been said about cutting refined sugar out of your diet, but in fact it is almost impossible to live in the twentieth century and not consume a certain amount of sugar as nearly everything you can buy seems to contain it. By avoiding obviously highly sugared foods and those known to contain large quantities of hidden sugar, you will be cutting down sufficiently to make that vital difference to the healthiness of your diet.

It is also too easy to become obsessive about fats. For example, if you go to a restaurant it is easy to choose new potatoes instead of chips, but if you are out to dinner and your hostess puts knobs of butter on the potatoes, don't refuse them for that reason. Cheerfully enjoying a little butter along with the hospitality and companionship of your friends is the most important thing.

Once you have a weight problem, you will retain the tendency to put on weight for the rest of your life. The only way you are going to be able to live happily with the fat person that is always somewhere inside trying to get out, is to change your whole attitude to food and the way you eat. There is no need to think that you will never be able to go out to dinner again because you will be on a permanent diet. Most restaurants have a menu that caters for a wide variety of tastes – after all, there are plenty of people around who actually dislike chips, fried food, pies, puddings and sweets. Where do they go to dinner? Look around for the sort of restaurant that serves simple meat dishes without sauces, along with fresh vegetables and salads. These dishes are just as easy to order as pie and chips.

If you are invited to a dinner party, point out to your hostess before you go that there are certain foods you don't eat. If you suffered from something like stomach ulcers you would have to make these arrangements, so regard your eating problem as a similar form of bodily malfunction and don't feel awkward. If you know certain foods trigger off an eating binge, do not be ashamed to inform your hostess that you cannot eat these foods. There is no necessity to go into great details of why, and she will probably be quite happy to fit in with your requirements.

Laziness is often at the root of bad eating habits, particularly among young people away from home for the first time and living in a bedsit or college rooms. It is much easier to live on sweets, cakes and biscuits than to make sure of having a balanced meal with plenty of protein each day. Cafes and canteens don't help because their cheap meals usually include chips and puddings rather than fresh vegetables and fruit. After a time poor nutrition leads to loss of energy, making it even more difficult to make the effort involved to correct eating habits.

Like all the best rules and laws, these ten commandments have been devised after much observation and frequent practice. Those who have a true eating problem will never really get it under control unless they realise they have not been living and eating according to these guidelines. Of course nobody expects you to keep every rule all the time and never break one occasionally – you would not be human if you did not slip up now and again. However unless you are prepared to accept every one of the ten commandments and do your best to follow them faithfully in the weeks and months ahead there is really little point in you even reading any further in this book.

CHAPTER SIX

The Goodies and the Baddies

> I firmly believe that if the whole *materia medica*, as now used, could be sunk to the bottom of the sea, it would be all the better for mankind – and all the worse for the fishes.
>
> Oliver Wendel Holmes, 1842

In an ideal world, with no stress or pollution, and proper diet available for everyone, food would supply everything the body needed. Unfortunately too many things interfere with that perfect balance, some of which are outside influences and others are self-imposed. The 'goodies', such as vitamins, minerals and the subtle blend of basic nutrients that the body needs to function properly, have to be balanced against the 'baddies' which undermine health, such as smoking, alcohol and drugs.

The 'goodies': vitamins and minerals

Nutritious food contains minute amounts of organic substances called vitamins which are essential to the healthy functioning of the body. It also contains small quantities of chemical elements which are a part of the body's structure, some of which are also involved in metabolism. Vitamin A is needed for healthy skin and eyes, vitamin D for strong teeth and bones, vitamin C for healthy skin and quick healing. There is a whole range of B vitamins needed for the metabolism of carbohydrates, protein and fats known as thiamine, riboflavin, nicotinic acid, pantothenic acid and B6, while folic acid and B12 are needed for healthy blood. Vitamin K is needed for blood to clot after a cut.

The mineral potassium is needed for correct water balance within the body tissues, calcium builds teeth and bones, magnesium is involved in the transfer of energy in the cells and iron forms part of the haemoglobin of the blood which carries oxygen around the body. Iodine is needed to make thyroid hormones, and there are many more essential minerals, all with an important role to play.

Even the experts do not agree on the exact requirements of any nutrient for the body; in fact requirements can vary enormously from one person to another. For example, when you are pregnant you don't need to eat enough calories for two, but you do need to ensure you are taking in enough nutrients for one and a half bodies. During illness or convalescence larger amounts of most nutrients are needed for repair, and those who smoke a lot or take in large amounts of alcohol, coffee or tea will also require more. A diet with too much refined carbohydrate increases the need for B vitamins, and a diet rich in saturated fats needs to be balanced with extra polyunsaturated fats and this in turn requires extra vitamin E. High salt diets need extra potassium intake. There are many other interrelations, but problems only occur when diets lack the necessary variety.

Don't overdo it

Now that bottles of all sorts of vitamin and mineral supplements are freely sold over the counter at chemists and health food shops, it is very tempting to try and diagnose your own deficiencies and dose yourself accordingly. Unless you have a good basic understanding of the subject, this is not advisable. At best you could be wasting your money, at worst it is possible to produce harmful effects by overdosing on huge amounts of vitamins. However, it is good practice to take a multi-vitamin and mineral supplement until such time as you are eating a truly healthy well-balanced diet. Some people, such as vegetarians and vegans and those on restricted diets should take supplements on a long-term basis.

If your tiredness is due to anaemia, this should be treated by a doctor; he will know if you need extra iron, folic acid and B12 or whether the root of your problem is overwork, worry or some medical condition. Vitamin C is the only vitamin which experts still believe to be safe to take in large amounts, but even this probably has an upper safety limit. However if your body seems to require the equivalent of a lorry load of oranges each day to keep it healthy, this points to something wrong at a deeper level which may need medical attention.

If you have a good, well-balanced diet of nutritious foods and avoid the things which deplete the body of its nutrients at an unnatural rate, you should take in automatically sufficient of the essential basics, without any fear of overdosing. However, a diet that consists mainly of junk food cannot be balanced to form a healthy diet, because the vitamin level in such food is so low.

Certain manufactured foods have nutrients added, such as vitamin A and D in margarine, calcium and vitamin B in bread. The following list shows foods that can be classed as 'junk' food because of their low nutrient level in comparison to calories. They are listed in descending order, with the more acceptable first, sinking to the nutritionally useless.

> Raisins and sultanas
> home-made cakes
> minced beef
> Yorkshire pudding
> steak pie (shop bought)
> beer
> chips (frozen)
> streaky bacon (well-grilled)
> pork sausage (well-grilled)
> sausage roll (home-made)
> white bread
> chocolate (milk or plain)
> digestive biscuits
> butter
> salami (or other fatty meats)
> cakes (iced fancies, shop-bought)
> pork pie (shop-bought)
> Mars bars (or similar)
> rice (white)

fruit pie (shop-bought)
jam
honey
Lucozade
coffee whiteners (e.g. Coffee Mate)
fat from meats (including lard)
packet desserts
jellies (shop-bought)
sugar (white, brown or rainbow coloured)

Even the most nutritious foods vary in the amount of minerals and vitamins they supply for the body's use. The fresher the food and the less it is cooked, the greater its nutritional value. Always cook vegetables for as short a time as possible, and in the minimum of water, so they remain firm and crisp. Better still, steam them or wrap them in foil and bake them in the oven to preserve maximum vitamin value. Best of all, eat them raw.

In Chart 6.1, those foods are listed that are exceptionally high in vitamins and minerals in relation to calories, while Chart 6.2 shows some of the main sources for the various vitamins and minerals required daily by the body.

The 'baddies'

Smoking
Smoking comes first among the baddies because it is such a common form of drug taking. Although most smokers are aware of the well-publicised facts about smoking, such as its relation to lung cancer, many do not know that smoking has far more widespread detrimental effects on the body.

Each cigarette is known to use up vitamin C from the body at the rate of 25 milligrammes per cigarette, so if you are a smoker vitamin C tablets are recommended to counteract this. The chewable ones make a substitute for sweets, give something to chew on and also get rid of the taste left in the mouth by smoking.

Obviously you would be healthier if you did not smoke, but if you are an habitual smoker this is not the time to think about giving it up. It is impossible to give up smoking *and* get over your

The Goodies and the Baddies
Chart 6.1 Foods exceptionally high in vitamins and minerals

Vegetables/salads	Protein foods	Fruits	Miscellaneous
Parsley	Ox liver	Blackcurrants	Yeast
Watercress	Chicken liver	Lemon juice	Bovril
Broccoli	Lamb's liver	Blackberries	Marmite
Peppers (green or red)	Lamb's kidney		
Brussels Sprouts			
Cauliflower			
Carrots			
Asparagus			
Tomatoes			
Lettuce			
Mushrooms			

Chart 6.2 Sources of specific vitamins and minerals

Vitamin A	Fish-liver oil
	Cheese
	Coloured fruits and vegetables
	Egg yolk
	Liver
	Cream and butter
Vitamin B complex	Wheat germ
	Yeast
	Whole-grain breads
	Cereals
Vitamin C	Orange, grapefruit and tomato juice
	Salads
	Raw vegetables and fruit
Vitamin D	Fish-liver oil
	Herrings, pilchards, tuna, mackerel and sardines
Vitamin E	Wheat germ
	Green leafy vegetables
	Vegetable oil
Riboflavin	Milk, cheese
	Eggs
	Meat
Pyridoxine	Liver
	Vegetables
	Bran
	Blackstrap molasses
Niacin	Whole-grain cereals
	Legumes
Vitamin K	Green leafy vegetables
	Blackstrap molasses

Calcium	Milk and cheese
	Green leafy vegetables
	Nuts
Phosphorous	Milk and cheese
	Meat
	Fish
	Eggs
	Whole-wheat cereals
Iron	Wheat germ
	Egg yolk
	Red meats
	Cocoa
	Whole-grain cereals
	Green vegetables
Copper	Egg yolk
	Cocoa
	Liver
	Nuts
Sodium, chlorine and iodine	Iodized (table) salt
Trace elements	Vegetables
	Sea foods
	Blackstrap molasses

Chart adapted from information in *Let's Stay Healthy* by Adelle Davis (Unwin Paperbacks).

eating problems at the same time, so concentrate on your eating first, and once that is under control and you begin to feel generally better and healthier, you may want to tackle your smoking habits in a year or so.

Alcohol and caffeine
Although both these substances are widely used by most of the population, they are still dangerous and addictive drugs if taken in excess. For this reason it is strongly emphasised that both must be avoided absolutely when embarking on the eating plan. Only when eating has been brought under control might it be safe to begin introducing them again in moderation. There are organisations to help people addicted to alcohol and to hard drugs such as heroin, but there is little done about the many drugs – pain relievers, diuretics, laxatives and so on – which can be bought across the counter and are considered harmless. These can be disastrous to the body if they are abused.

Salt

Over the past few years a lot has been spoken and written about the effects of salt in the diet. On the one hand is the old fashioned 'salt of the earth' view that this is something precious to man; on the other it is condemned as an enemy to health. Sometimes it can get confusing trying to decide which 'expert' to believe.

As far as weight is concerned, it is a fact that too much salt intake does mean a tendency to retain water, but to what extent will depend on individual body metabolism. We probably eat a lot more salt than we realise. It is not just what we sprinkle over a meal or add during cooking, but so many foods contain large amounts of hidden salt, things which don't seem to taste at all salty, like certain breakfast cereals, for example (see Chart 6.3). Another good reason for eating as much fresh food as possible and cutting down on processed foods.

Chart 6.3   *Foods high in salt*

All-bran	Omelette
Bacon	Ox tongue (cooked)
Bacon joints	Oxo cubes
Baking powder	Piccalilli
Beef sausages	Pork sausages
Black pudding	Prawns
Bovril	Processed cheese
Camembert	Rice Krispies
Cheese spread	Salami
Chopped pork	Salt
Cockles	Scrambled egg
Cornflakes	Shrimps
Danish blue type cheese	Smoked cod
Gammon joint	Smoked haddock
Gammon rashers	Smoked salmon
Ham	Stilton
Instant potato	Sweet pickle
Jellied veal	Tinned crab
Luncheon meat	Tomato ketchup
Marmite	Tongue
Oatcakes	Welsh rarebit
Olives in brine	Winkles

Fats

The human body can't live without fat, but although Eskimos live on little else and remain extremely healthy, the majority of us consume far more than our bodies require. For those watching their weight this is disastrous – pound for pound fat is the most fattening food there is.

The effects of fats on health is a subject that has been widely researched and much of the resulting information is rather contradictory. In general unsaturated fats such as corn oil and fish oils are better for the health than saturated fats such as lard and butter, but for the weight watcher both are equally high in calories. If you are eating out always try to choose an alternative to fried foods, and at home always grill, bake or steam. Remember oil is also a fat and discover alternative ways of making tasty salad dressings.

Chart 6.4 *Hidden fats*

	% of fat		% of fat
Pork Pie individual	27.0	Peanut butter (smooth)	53.7
Steak and Kidney Pie individual	21.2	Walnuts	51.5
Sardines in oil	28.3	Bacon back rashers, grilled	33.8
Fried scampi	17.6	Beefburgers, fried	17.3
Cheddar type cheese	33.5	Rump steak, grilled lean only	6.0
Cream cheese	47.4	Oil	99.9
Sausage roll flaky pastry	36.2	Mayonnaise	78.9
Pork sausages grilled	24.6	Corned beef	12.1
Peanuts	49.0	Milk chocolate	30.3
Avocado pear	22.2	Low-fat spread	40.7
Butter	82.0	Fresh whole milk	3.8
Roast leg pork lean only	6.9	Ice cream, dairy	6.6
Grilled lamb chop lean only	12.3	Crisps	35.9
Kipper baked	11.4	Roast potatoes	4.8
Roast lamb lean only	16.6	Whole raw egg	10.9
Loin pork chop grilled lean only	10.7	Single cream	21.2
Onions, fried	33.3	Chocolate biscuits, full coated	27.6
Currant bun	7.6	Cottage cheese	4.0
Roast chicken meat only	5.4	Salad cream	27.4
Whole mushrooms, fried	22.3	Cream crackers	16.3
Fruit pie, pastry top and bottom	15.5		

Taken from '*The Composition of Foods*' by A. A. Paul and D. A. T. Southgate

Watch out for hidden fats in such things as pastry – beware of the 'healthy' quiche which is loaded with fat. There are plenty of ways of cutting down on fat intake without even drastically changing your favourite meals, but at the same time never become obsessive about a tiny knob of butter on the peas when mother-in-law invites you to Sunday lunch. Keep everything in proportion, and maintain a relaxed attitude, then the fats will take care of themselves.

Laxatives

As so many compulsive eaters and bulimics have learnt to their cost, taking laxatives is an easy habit to slip into. It is also a very common habit. Taking a laxative occasionally when needed is no more harmful than having the occasional glass of wine. With all such things the problem comes when they are taken to excess ... a bottle of whisky a day, a huge binge every day, 150 laxatives a day.

Compulsive eaters often take laxatives in the mistaken belief that they will reduce their weight. If the scales do show a weight loss, it is because the body has lost water and fibre, not fat, so it is an artificial loss which will return as soon as they eat again. The real problem is that essential vitamins and minerals are also lost, or not taken up by the body, leading to malnutrition and debility. Also the more laxatives are abused, the more they become needed because the intestinal muscles lose their tone causing constipation. Indeed, abusing laxatives in a vain attempt to achieve a flat stomach only has the opposite effect; they tend to make the abdomen blow out and look bigger, and they also encourage hunger pangs to return more quickly than if the intestines had been allowed to empty naturally.

If use and abuse of laxatives is only a minor problem, it is recommended to gradually reduce the number taken until it is down to one or two a day. However if the abuse is severe, it is important to consult your doctor. Do not try to cut them out suddenly as this will be too great a shock to your body. Plenty of bran, water and fibrous food will help, but if it does not lead to normal bowel movements after a few weeks, again consult a doctor.

Diuretics

Diuretics are often prescribed by doctors for such conditions as premenstrual tension and high blood pressure. If used correctly, they can be very beneficial in certain cases. Diuretics are also sold over the counter for premenstrual tension, and although these can also be beneficial in certain conditions, they are often abused by compulsive eaters and bulimics. In a similar way to laxatives, abuse of diuretics leads to loss of essential minerals and vitamins, in particular potassium. Lack of potassium leads to sugar cravings, which in turn creates bingeing, weight gain and the urge to take more laxatives and diuretics: a never-ending circle. Diuretics can also cause severe dehydration leading to kidney problems – it is not unknown for a kidney to be lost in cases of extreme abuse – and overdosing on diuretics has also resulted in heart attack.

Sleeping tablets

If night eating is a problem, taking sleeping pills will not help and can make the trouble worse as it is easier to binge when you are in a drugged state and unable to exert self-control. In extreme cases it is possible to eat while asleep.

Ask yourself why you aren't sleeping. Do you wake at 2 am, possibly because you are clinically depressed? In which case seek medical help. Quite possibly you wake because you are hungry, so take a hard look at your eating pattern.

If you can't get to sleep because you are worried or your brain is overactive, do something to sort out the cause of this anxiety. Are you tired? Not everyone needs the traditional eight hours sleep. Perhaps you would benefit from taking more exercise during the day.

Birth control pill

The oral contraceptive pill is often blamed for weight gain. An experiment conducted using two groups of rats showed that the group given the hormone progesterone (a key ingredient of the pill) gained weight, compared with the untreated group. They gained weight in three ways: water, which disappeared quickly if the pill was discontinued, muscle and similar protein tissue, which disappeared less rapidly than the water, and fat which

72

only went away after reduced calorie intake or increased activity. Further experiments with the rats showed this fat was at least partly due to their becoming less active. Although these findings apply to rats rather than humans, it is advised that anyone going on the pill makes a modest cut in calorie intake or increases their amount of exercise to avoid this fat gain.

Thyroid hormones

Thyroid hormones are no longer used to treat obesity because it has been shown that their effect is similar to going on a dangerous crash diet. Much of the weight lost is protein tissue which causes a slower metabolic rate, leading to a rapid regain of weight, especially fatty tissue.

Symptoms of thyroid deficiency include cold skin, hair falling out and a lowered metabolic rate, which can also appear as the result of poor quality low calorie diets and can sometimes lead to a faulty diagnosis by a doctor. But even genuine cases of low thyroid need to eat carefully and follow a high protein, high nutrient diet rather than expect the drugs alone to solve their problems. Thyroid taken when there is no thyroid deficiency causes the thyroid gland to stop working and thus creates a need for the tablets. Thyroid taken in excessive dosages causes serious side effects and heart conditions have been known to occur.

Anti-depressants

If you have suffered a great loss or a distressing experience of some sort, it is only natural that you should grieve and feel unhappy. Drugs that artificially bottle up those emotions are creating a time bomb that will explode sooner or later and may well be expressed by eating problems. If a false sense of well-being is induced by drugs, this can lead to eating more and putting on weight. Some anti-depressants are believed to affect the appetite centre of the brain, increasing appetite and causing a craving for carbohydrate foods. If you are taking anti-depressants, aim to cut them down, but do this in consultation with your doctor. Never just stop taking them abruptly as this can lead to unpleasant side effects. If you are having trouble cutting down on these pills, you can get help from one of the special societies, such as TRANEX who can give expert advice (see Appendix II for the address).

Tranquillisers
Tranquillisers do not get rid of a problem, they only mask it. If a compulsive eater tells her doctor she is depressed, but does not mention her eating problem she may be given tranquillisers and then walk around in a stupor and binge more than ever because she is not fully in control of herself. Tranquillisers will not cure an eating problem, nor a bad marriage, nor an unhappy working environment. These are problems which need to be faced and worked out, not blotted out by drugs.

Slimming pills
Although the amphetamines which were proved physically addictive are no longer available (except from unscrupulous sources only interested in your money, not your well-being), any slimming pill can easily become psychologically or even physically addictive. At the Maisner Centre, we see many people whose life has grown to revolve around these expensive pills; they are unable to give them up, or if they do they suffer horrific withdrawal symptoms.

SUSAN had been taking so-called non-addictive slimming pills for years. They cost her £40 a week and she had to work an extra shift to pay for her addiction. Whilst attempting to get her eating habits under control she stopped taking the slimming pills and plunged into a suicidal state. A few days later at a workshop session she was a wreck, depressed, crying and shaking, but in time she did manage to get over it although it took her over a year to get out of debt and she still carries resentment for the years she feels the pills took out of her life.

ANN was at that workshop where she met Susan at the height of her struggle to break the slimming pill addiction. Yet even after such a lesson she began taking them herself. She told herself she would just take them for a week or so, just to get rid of the weight she had put on during her recent session of bingeing. Of course, before long she too was 'hooked', paying out large amounts of money each week for slimming pills.

JOAN has been taking slimming pills for about 20 years, and she still weighs 19 stone.

Slimming pills are just another excuse for not getting to grips with what is at the root of your eating problems. In the back of your mind you tell yourself it is all right to binge, you can then lose the extra weight by taking the pills. On slimming pills you crash diet with all the disastrous consequences to blood sugar levels and metabolic rate already explained.

Many compulsive eaters were set on the road to eating problems by taking slimming pills. Overweight people lose touch with what real hunger is, they do not learn how to eat properly without artificial help, and so when the course of pills ends, they either regain the weight lost or get depressed because weight loss is slower.

As bingeing in many cases has nothing to do with hunger, you can still binge while on slimming pills. In fact, there are so many bad features to slimming pills that everyone is warned to leave them alone.

CHAPTER SEVEN

Isolating Your Trigger Foods

One man's meat is another man's poison.

A true allergy causes the body to produce antibodies that create physical symptoms, such as a rash from eating strawberries. With the compulsive eater an intolerance to certain foods may not be a true allergy but a form of reaction that triggers them off on a binge. Once triggered off in this way, the compulsive eater will continue to eat anything within reach until the binge has run its course. The foods that have this effect on compulsive eaters are called trigger foods.

Often the trigger food is something the compulsive eater does not even like, but feels compelled to eat. Most compulsive eaters are familiar with the sorts of food that can cause a binge. Rarely is it something low-caloried, like oranges or celery, although apples surprisingly are a common trigger food. It is more likely to be refined carbohydrates like pies, cakes and biscuits, and in particular cereals and in some cases dairy products.

Hot and cold sweats, especially during the night, invariably point to some sort of food intolerance. If you suffer from these, check your charts to see if you have eaten a lot of some food or something unusual that day. Such apparently unrelated symptoms can go for years without their true cause being discovered. It is not unusual for a woman to be told her hot sweats are due to the menopause and she accepts this without associating them with her eating problem.

Headaches can also be caused by intolerance to certain foods.

Again check your chart to see what you have been eating. Chocolate, sweets, alcohol and cheese can cause headaches, for instance, so if your doctor can find no medical reason for your problem, consider carefully whether there might be any connection with your eating problem. (Some doctors now believe the cause of most migraines to be allergies to foods.)

Research at the Maisner Centre for Eating Disorders has shown that changing to the eating plan with its balanced nutrition and emphasis on stabilising blood sugar levels has, in many cases, resulted in the disappearance of many true allergies, including hay fever.

Trigger foods

The first step in isolating trigger foods is to examine your weekly food charts. Perhaps your binges begin with a bowl of breakfast cereal, in particular muesli, which is a great cause of bingeing. This may come as a surprise, because muesli is generally promoted as being so good for you, and it is something you buy from the health food shop.

It is often difficult to know exactly what food is good for you and what is not, especially when advertising and television bombard everyone regularly with information about what they should and should not be eating. The important point to remember is that an advertisement is aimed at selling a product, that is the one and only reason manufacturers spend thousands of pounds on advertising, and they will twist the facts to suit their product and convince you to buy it. They are unlikely to tell you that their product will cause a binge a day!

It is also easy to assume that anything bought from a health food shop is good for you, but that depends on what it is and how you make use of it. It is probably true to say that such items are sometimes less harmful than the equivalent bought from the supermarket. However it is not unknown for people to buy a date and walnut cake and believe it is not fattening because it came from the health food shop rather than the supermarket. Another dangerous mistake people make is to think that brown sugar is good for you – all sugar is bad, whether white, brown or multicoloured.

Muesli in small amounts is a better breakfast for many people than a bowl of cornflakes or white bread toasted with marmalade. But as far as the compulsive eater is concerned it is something to be strictly avoided. It contains various items that are known to trigger off binges, such as cereal and dried fruit, so don't have it in the house.

Dried fruit is a very important trigger food; again check your charts to see if this could be your trigger. It is sweet, it is also high in calories, and it is easy to nibble from the packet or buy as fruit cake.

PAULINE managed to get her eating under control, but knew dried fruit was her trigger food and made sure she kept well away from it. Out of interest one Christmas she decided to try a controlled experiment of eating one mince-pie to see what would happen. The result was she immediately had to eat the rest of the packet of mince-pies and had there been a Christmas cake in the house she would have started on that as well. After a successful period without bingeing, a small amount of her trigger food set her off again.

Once you know what your trigger foods are, the only answer is to avoid them. Try not to have them in the house and make a point of never, never buying them when out shopping. If you have to have them in the house, keep them somewhere out of sight and always be aware that they are the trigger that can set off a binge.

JANE knew the dangers of muesli to her eating habits, but made the excuse that her husband liked it so she had to buy it. In fact she was the one who could not leave it alone, and her husband, when asked, said he would be quite happy to give up muesli for breakfast if it would help his wife. Having it in the house for her husband was just an excuse for bingeing on Jane's part.

A trigger food does not always trigger off a binge, which can make it difficult to recognise which are your trigger foods at first. Some foods only trigger a binge if eaten excessively. If you only eat strawberry ice cream occasionally when you go to the beach it may have no effect, but if you buy a big tub of it and eat some every day for a week it could trigger a binge. Artificial additives, particularly colourings, can act as a trigger. For example, one compulsive eater found she could eat vanilla ice cream but raspberry ripple triggered a binge because her body was intolerant to the red substance used for colouring.

FELICITY liked to eat a few grapes after dinner and they did not cause any problem to her, but gradually the amount of grapes began to creep up until she found she was eating 2 pounds of them after her meal and she felt unable to stop. She managed to cut out grapes completely and felt much better. Her problem was that grapes were only a semi-trigger, and only began to cause her an eating problem when she ate them every day. After a while she was able to go back to eating grapes occasionally, but was careful never to have them for more than one day in a row.

Once a trigger food is recognised, it is still not easy to avoid eating it. Try to say to yourself, 'If I eat this food, it will make me binge and I don't want to do that.' Have a substitute food handy which you can eat without disastrous effects. If alcohol is your trigger, always have fruit juice or soda water in the house and avoid drinks that hang around in half empty bottles.

If you know that a food is a trigger to a binge, ask yourself why you want it, after all it might well be something you don't even like. The answer is likely to be quite near the surface.

CHAPTER EIGHT

Coping with Stress

What is this life, if full of care
We have no time to stand and stare?
No time to stand beneath the boughs
And stare as long as sheep or cows.
'Leisure'
W. H. Davies 1870–1940

In the twentieth century stress is given as the cause of almost everything that is wrong with man. It is blamed for the business man's heart attack and the housewife's nervous breakdown. Children and even family pets are said to suffer from stress. It is hardly surprising that every compulsive eater who has visited the Maisner Centre when asked if she suffers from stress answered, 'Yes.'

What exactly is stress?

Watch a wild bird that visits your garden for bread you have thrown out on a winter's day. All the time it is on the ground feeding it is tense and alert, continually looking all around for any danger. If a cat appears on the garden fence, it immediately spreads its wings and flies away. That bird is under stress: all its faculties of observation and self-preservation are working to full capacity because it faces danger. Basically man is designed the same way. As a primitive animal he had to be constantly on the alert when out hunting, ready to stand and fight or to run away as fast as possible when danger threatened. At the first sign of danger his heartbeat would quicken, blood pressure rise and hormone output increase to ensure extra energy-producing sugar reached muscles and brain. Red blood cells worked extra hard taking in oxygen and getting rid of carbon dioxide, and the digestive processes turned off so that all energies would be directed towards meeting the danger.

In times of extreme danger people still react in the same way. There is no shortage of tales about people accomplishing almost impossible feats when their life was threatened, athletes breaking world records when faced with tough competition. In times of war soldiers push themselves physically beyond anything they would expect in peace time and win victories against great odds. But for the majority of people today technology provides a degree of physical security; we don't have to grapple with tigers, hunt down food in a forest or face starvation, or even live out of doors in the worst weather. Life is easy, we are protected from danger and physical exertion.

However, when we feel threatened or under strain, our bodies still react chemically in the same way as they did in the jungle. When you have a pile of typing to get through, the telephone keeps ringing and the boss is demanding coffee immediately, you are under pressure. If the baby is crying, the milk boiling over and the doorbell ringing, you are being attacked on all sides. All those extra hormones and red blood cells spring into action automatically, but instead of running two miles to the nearest cave for shelter, you react to modern stress by sorting things out with comparatively little physical exertion, thus not getting those extra chemicals out of the system.

Is stress a bad thing?

Without this automatic reaction to stress man would not have survived and developed. He would have been wiped out by stronger animals. Some people really seem to thrive on stress, they only show their worth when the going gets tough, and the bigger the problem the better they seem to handle things. Most people know that when something is really important to them they do it better, the added stress lends an edge to their abilities.

Everyone has a different level of stress which they can

tolerate, you probably know how much pressure you can take comfortably. It is only when stress tolerance is low, or stress levels too high in proportion to tolerance that stress becomes a problem.

Stress and food

The initial response to stress is alarm, 'I am in danger, I must prepare to fight or run away.' The oldest and most commonly used tranquilliser in times of alarm is food, and so it is very easy to turn to food at times of stress. Most compulsive eaters know their eating problems are always worse when things are going badly for them, and many go to elaborate lengths to avoid putting themselves into situations of stress, in particular when these involve relationships.

It is the very basic threat of not getting enough to eat that makes a baby scream, go red in the face and wave her arms and legs around when she feels hungry. Being given food and love together quickly reassures a baby, but if left to cry or given food without the proper love and attention, she begins to associate all sorts of additional emotional reactions with the original instinct of stress when food is needed.

It is so often found that people who basically feel they are not getting what they deserve in life, those with dependency problems, also have eating problems. They have never learnt to cope with that original reaction to stress they were born with and so wanting quite literally makes them hungry.

What to do about stress

One very good way of dealing with the result of a stressful situation is to do as our primitive ancestors did, follow through with the physical response that the body was primed for. That does not mean grabbing a club and beating your boss over the head, but if you have had a stressful day at the office, go to an energetic exercise class, out for a run, a swim or even a brisk walk. If the children are driving you mad, spring clean the spare bedroom or make a loaf of bread and knead it vigorously. It is amazing how physical exercise can work on frustrations and help put problems in proportion. Where stress is more of a long-term build up rather than the result of one particular situation, talking is a great help in releasing pent up tensions. If you feel you cannot talk to close family or friends, your family doctor could help, although he has his own load of stress and does not always have the time to give you all the support you need. The Samaritans are always anonymously at the end of a telephone to listen for as long as you want to talk when stress seems overwhelming, and most areas have self-help groups where people with similar problems can get together and talk. If there is not one near you why not start one? Put an advertisement in the local paper inviting other compulsive eaters to get together.

Yoga is an excellent way of learning to relax and overcome stress, although many people find it is difficult to switch off at first. A beginners class with a qualified teacher of yoga will introduce you gradually to techniques of breathing and relaxation which you can practise at any time when you feel under stress. Other forms of mental relaxation, such as meditation and self-hypnosis, are an invaluable way of discovering release from tension, but they should not be plunged into without proper knowledge and preparation. Join a group or seek out a teacher where there is a genuine desire to spread light and peace in the world, because even in this area there are those whose main concern is to make money from other people's ignorance.

Advanced yoga and meditation are designed to progress you further on a healing path, not to help you block out unbearable problems. Too many people get caught up in religion or meditation because they cannot cope with life and are looking for an easy way out. Begin basic yoga techniques now and when you have sorted out your life and your eating problems you can then progress to become a healthier, calmer and happier person than you ever thought possible.

Owning a pet has been proved to be a great help in reducing stress. Stroking a cat has a very calming effect, even watching fish swim in a tank is relaxing, which is why you sometimes find fish tanks in dentists' waiting rooms.

It is not possible to remove stress from your life, especially if you want to live a full and sociable life, both at work and at home. Aim to raise your stress threshold by becoming less tense and more confident about your ability to handle situations.

Stress tapes
The Maisner Centre produces audio tapes aimed at helping compulsive eaters combat stress and stressful situations. These are obtainable from the centre, whose address can be found at the beginning of the book.

CHAPTER NINE

The Benefits of Exercise

'But wait a bit,' the oysters cried,
'Before we have our chat;
For some of us are out of breath,
And all of us are fat.'

Lewis Carroll

Pity the poor fat oysters, they puffed along behind the Walrus and the Carpenter but only got eaten in the end. Sooner or later if you are overweight, you have to face the consequences.

Being overweight puts a strain on the heart and all the body's organs, and just carrying that extra fat around takes extra calories, which is one reason why severely overweight people tend to lose weight more rapidly than those with only a little extra. Just existing uses up more energy. To lose weight it is necessary to consume fewer calories. Just increasing the amount of exercise without reducing the food intake would take a huge amount of jogging, press ups or swimming each day to make a small impression. If you are overweight, you will have a lot of extra fat, but it is also possible to be overfat without actually being overweight.

Animals that are bred for meat are encouraged to take as little exercise as possible so that their steaks and chops, once served at the table, will have a good layer of fat running through them. Animals that have plenty of freedom or work for a living have much tougher meat with muscle and sinew in place of fatty deposits.

The human body is the same; fat will be deposited deep in the tissues as well as in the more obvious places such as abdomen and thighs. The more fat is allowed to linger within the body and around the organs the less efficiently that body will function, especially in areas such as the heart and kidneys. This is why exercise is so vitally important, not so much as a way of losing weight but as a means of improving the quality of the body tissues' make-up.

Will exercise make me weigh less?

Not necessarily. Exercise builds muscles which are weighty and as muscle replaces fat the balance of weight may not be altered noticeably. However muscle takes up less space than fat so you will notice a difference in your measurements and the way your clothes fit. Exercise can also redistribute weight, as flab in unwanted places is replaced by muscle tissue lying close to the framework of the body.

Why exercise?

As every dieter knows it is possible to lose weight by careful dieting. The real problem comes when the diet is over and the pounds start creeping back. This is where exercise can help. Sensible eating combined with regular exercise creates a healthy body, less likely to regain unwanted weight. A healthy body also improves the quality of the emotional and mental state, helping to cope with the emotional problems that lead to compulsive eating. Exercise not only makes you feel good, it makes you look good. You are more alive, happier and more self-confident.

The fitter you get and the more in tune with your body, the more likely you are to turn away from the wrong foods and begin to prefer the foods that are good for you. You will be more likely to eat only when you experience real hunger and after a good exercise workout you are not so likely to be tempted to nibble. When you have used your body hard, you will find that you can more easily relax and will sleep more soundly. Over a period of time regular aerobic exercise can increase the body's metabolic rate.

Man is a member of the animal kingdom and in his primitive state had to hunt for miles over rough ground for his food. The human body is designed to be exercised and functions more efficiently if pushed hard regularly rather than over-cossetted.

I don't need exercise; I am always on the go

Rushing around the shops, ironing a pile of shirts or standing behind a shop counter all day are physically tiring, but they cannot be described as exercise. The kind of exercise that is really beneficial is the kind that elevates your heart rate to just over three-quarters of its maximum beats per minute and at the same time makes you breathe more deeply and more often. Gentle stretching helps to tone up the body, but aerobic exercise that gets oxygen right into the system is what is needed to get you really fit and healthy.

Aerobic classes are probably the most fun way to exercise, but swimming, cycling and jogging are also good aerobic exercises. For an exercise to be truly aerobic, it has to be done for a minimum of 12 minutes, once the heart is at its training rate. Most people should be looking for a training heart rate of between 140 and 170 beats per minute. Your maximum heart rate is 220 beats per minute minus your age or thereabouts and your training rate is 80 per cent of this. To check your pulse lay the tip of one finger gently on the inside of your wrist, about ½ inch from the outer edge. Take the pulse for six seconds, then add a zero for beats per minute.

Chart 9.1   *Will help you assess your training rate*

Age	Maximum heart rate Beats per minute	Recommended training rate Beats per minute
20	200	160
30	190	152
40	182	146
50	175	140

Recommended training rate based on resting heart rates of 72 for males and 80 for females

If you have not exercised recently, are overweight, over 40, have any medical condition especially a history of heart disease, do consult your doctor before taking up any form of vigorous exercise. It is not recommended that you exercise after you have been bingeing.

For the best all-year-round results in terms of burning calories, controlling weight and getting fitter, you should exercise aerobically three to four times a week. Going to aerobic classes has the added benefits of getting you out of the house, away from food, and also helps to alleviate boredom and loneliness. Don't be put off by the thought that everyone else at the class will be young and slim and fit; some will be, of course, especially the instructor – it wouldn't be much of an advertisement for her classes if she wasn't.

It is important to have the courage to join in a class and work at your own pace, not try and keep up with the ballet student standing next to you. You will win the admiration of the class by sticking at it and showing a gradual weight loss and improvement in your looks. If the class you go to does make you feel fat and foolish that is the fault of the teacher; go and find another class where they are more friendly and sympathetic.

It is a good idea to go to a proper experienced teacher where the classes are not too large. It is possible to cause damage and discomfort if you exercise at home in the wrong way. Don't overdo it the first time and then give up; regular exercise within your own capabilities is what is needed. It is the same idea as eating regular, proper sized meals instead of bingeing and starving.

What are the benefits of aerobic exercise?

1. When you exercise you burn more calories than when you sit still. That sounds obvious, but in fact the result is much more subtle. Because everybody's metabolism is speeded up while you are exercising, you will continue to burn more calories for up to an hour after your workout, so the immediate effect is doubled. In addition regular exercise actually changes the body's basic metabolic rate making it easier to stop extra pounds creeping on.
2. Your body will shed excess fat and develop attractive strong

muscles. Unless you intend to become an Olympic athlete you will not be too muscle bound to interfere with femininity, you will just say goodbye to ugly flab. Muscle tissue actually burns more calories than fat even when you are not moving about.

3. You will look more attractive generally, your body will become more shapely and leaner, you will look healthier and your posture will improve as your body gets stronger.

4. You will feel great. Exercise causes your body to release natural substances that make you feel quite 'high'. Exercise is one of the best anti-depressants there is.

5. You will become physically fitter. Your heart and lungs will become more efficient and healthier, resulting in your having more stamina and energy for everything in your life. Fit people live longer.

'I just don't like the idea of aerobics classes'

Still unconvinced about the miracles aerobic exercise can do? Ask yourself why. Perhaps you have your own reasons for not wanting to lose weight and look and feel good. If you feel fitter, you might have to start tackling some of those other problem areas of your life.

Perhaps you feel embarrassed because you are overweight. You don't have to pour yourself into a skimpy leotard and glossy tights, wear something loose and comfortable to begin with or choose slimming black rather than bright fashionable colours. There will be girls there with lovely figures, but they will be too busy admiring themselves in the long mirrors to look at you. Let them be an inspiration to you; keep up the exercise regularly and you can look like that one day.

Don't accept the old excuse about being too busy for classes. What else are you doing with that time, watching television? Bingeing?

If you still cannot bring yourself to join a class, take up another form of exercise. You can go jogging without anyone seeing you, or visit the swimming pool. Even a good long brisk walk with plenty of fresh air is excellent exercise. The more you exercise, the more you will want to ... so start today.

CHAPTER TEN

The Body Clock

To everything there is a season,
and a time to every purpose under the heaven.
Ecclesiastes (iii) 1

The whole universe is totally rhythmic; everything from the smallest atom to the solar system moves in its own cycle and creates the grand harmony of existence. Man has his own place in this great scheme of things, and is subject to the same laws of nature that govern every part of life, therefore he too is totally rhythmic.

Modern life with its artificial ways is in danger of disturbing this order of things, and allowing man to get out of touch with his body rhythms. Animals know when to sleep, when to eat more and what foods to avoid because they are bad for them, but man seems to have lost this natural knowledge and keeps unnatural hours and eats the sort of things his body was never designed to cope with.

Electric light and power means we no longer have to cease work when it gets dark or slow down our pace during the winter months. Machinery can run for 24 hours a day without resting and so men are expected to work alongside them, day and night. Many shops and factories work seven days a week, so the old custom of Sunday as a day of rest has largely disappeared. In fact Sunday is now the opportunity for more frantic activity than any other day of the week.

Your life should have a natural rhythm to it, something that you recognise and become familiar with, then your body will work more efficiently. If you sleep a lot one day, then stay up all night, then take a short nap the following afternoon, your rhythm of sleep is disturbed. In the same way if you starve yourself for two or three days, then binge, then binge again, then starve, you are destroying the natural digestive rhythms of your body.

Your body is a complicated clock with different cycles for every 24 hours, every month and every year. It is rather like a complicated time clock on the central heating system, if you fiddle about with it, the whole system starts to go wrong. The radiators turn themselves off when you come home in the evening and on when you are going to bed, they come on in mid-summer and go off on Christmas Day. So although you have an expensive and efficient central heating system, you are not getting the best out of it.

The body clock is just the same – mess about with its natural rhythms and it won't work efficiently.

Setting your time clock

First of all, take a close look at your life and work out what your natural body rhythms are, then you can assess how you should be setting your personal body clocks to get your body working to peak efficiency. For example, if you have small children you will probably have to get up early, so don't sit up late at night watching television or alternatively arrange for you all to have a proper siesta every day.

Consider at what time of day you feel your hungriest. If it is always around 11 am, arrange to have your lunch early; if it is 2 am, lay out a low-calorie nourishing meal for yourself before you go to bed. Listen to what your body is trying to tell you and set your body clocks accordingly.

Pepping yourself up with too much black coffee, cigarettes, alcohol and chocolates will confuse your natural rhythms and cause havoc with the natural way your body operates. Even a short time each day of complete relaxation, deep breathing and slowing down will make it easier to tune in to your own rhythms.

BARBARA always binges at ten in the evening. Because she has young children, she has tea with them at 5 pm, then when her husband comes home at 7 pm she cooks him a meal but is not really hungry herself, so she does not eat with him. By 10 pm she is hungry, and so she binges. Her answer is to re-organise her meals, to have a light tea with the children and eat her main meal with her husband, so she will not be hungry later in the evening.

The menstrual cycle

Many women blame a lot of their 'problems' on premenstrual tension. It can be the grand excuse for anything and everything, and some women seem to suffer from it for 28 days of the month. If you really have a medical problem your doctor or family planning clinic should be able to help, but perhaps you should also consider whether it might be just a front for other troubles, an excuse for giving in to moods and weakness.

The days before a period are often a difficult time for the compulsive eater and cravings for certain foods are sometimes much more apparent now. Nearly every woman, whether she has eating problems or not, gets a craving for sweet foods just before her period. This is so common, it can almost be considered normal. To help you become more aware of your individual pattern, complete the chart shown on p. 93, marking a cross in the appropriate box each time you crave food which is unplanned, whether you actually eat it or not. The numbers at the top of the chart indicate the days in your cycle, with day 1 as the first day of your period. Keep this record for at least three months. From the completed example (Chart 10.1b) it is easy to see that this woman suffers from more food cravings in the days just before her period is due, although it is not unusual for a woman to crave at other particular times throughout her cycle.

When you have built up a picture of the times you are most likely to crave unplanned foods and when you are likely to be feeling at your lowest because of premenstrual tension, you can plan ahead. Be extra nice to yourself on these days. Allow yourself to eat a bit more at that time; don't plan stressful meetings or exhausting jobs, this is no time to redecorate the

Chart 10.1a   *Food cravings in relation to the menstrual cycle*

1	2	3	4	5	6	7	8	9	10	11	12	13	14	15	16	17	18	19	20	21	22	23	24	25	26	27	28	
																												1st Month
																												2nd Month
																												3rd Month

Chart 10.1b   *An example*

1	2	3	4	5	6	7	8	9	10	11	12	13	14	15	16	17	18	19	20	21	22	23	24	25	26	27	28	
					×											×			×			×		×	×	×	× ×	1st Month
×										×										×			×	×	× ×		×	2nd Month
							×										×		×		×		×	× ×	×	×	×	3rd Month

To help you become more aware of your individual pattern, complete this chart, starting from the first day of your period EACH MONTH. Mark a cross in the appropriate box each time you crave food which is unplanned, whether or not you actually eat it. Numbers indicate the days in your cycle, i.e. 1 = the first day of your period, 2 the second, etc.

kitchen. Instead save up some special treat or outing that will make you feel good, like a visit to the hairdresser or time to sit down and read a favourite book.

Shift work

Nurses are more likely than any other group of people to become compulsive eaters or suffer from some form of eating problem. Look around that hospital ward and most of the nurses are either all skin and bone or well covered in spare flesh. One problem with nursing is, of course, the tendency to eat too much at strange times of the day and night and the wrong kinds of food, such as canteen chips and buns, plus chocolates from grateful patients. Changing shifts often involves fitting in extra meals, especially if there is a family at home to be catered for as well.

Another problem is that the irregular hours and night shifts upset the hormonal balance of the body and put the whole body clock out of balance. It also plays havoc with blood sugar levels and upsets the efficient working of the hypothalamus. This is believed to be the mechanism that initiates feelings of hunger when levels of glucose and nutrients in the body are low. It naturally works on a day and night cycle, relaxing at night to allow the body to rest undisturbed by appetite. Shift work interferes with this natural rhythm leading to feelings of hunger at unusual hours.

Night eating

True night eating is when a person goes to bed and to sleep, then wakes up during the night to eat. The main cause of night eating is nothing more mysterious than hunger. If you have not eaten enough during the day, the demands of your stomach will prevent you sleeping peacefully during the night. If you are following the eating plan, you will realise by now the importance of a snack last thing at night.

Food allergies can also cause night eating, as can addictions. For example, if you are taking in nicotine and caffeine all day long, the body will start to miss them if you go for several hours during sleep without a coffee or a cigarette. If it gets to this stage, you really should be doing something about your smoking and your coffee drinking to gradually wean the body off its addiction.

If you have trouble with your blood sugar level, this may drop very low while you are asleep and cause you to wake at around 2 am because you are hungry. This can happen if you have not been eating properly during the day, but if there is no obvious reason you should consult your doctor about your blood sugar level.

If there does not seem to be any obvious cause for your hunger except the fact that your body likes to be fed at that time, don't feel guilty, prepare a meal of salad and fruit that you can sit down and enjoy in the middle of the night. If possible have this meal ready in another room, so you do not have to go into the kitchen, where it will be too tempting to eat more than you need. You can ask someone to lock the kitchen for you, but only if you want them to, otherwise it could become a source of resentment. It is important to get to the root of your night hunger and deal with that, rather than try to use locked doors to try and force yourself to stop eating. A word of warning here, never lock yourself in your bedroom at night in case of an emergency, such as fire.

In really severe cases a compulsive eater may be so obsessed with food that she walks and eats in her sleep. This is very distressing and needs therapy to sort out as it is due to deep-lying emotional reasons.

Constant waking in the night may also be the result of too much control during the day. You may be constantly trying to control your eating, as well as fighting to keep in control in other areas of your life, such as your job or relationships. When half asleep, this control relaxes and the problems you have suppressed during the day, rise to the surface of your mind, waking you up. The battle to keep control during the day may also be reflected in dreams and nightmares which can disturb your sleep. (If you are always waking up but cannot remember your dreams, you may be having nightmares. A therapist may be able to help you if this is the case.)

Worry is a great robber of sleep. If you lie awake at night worrying you are sure to creep down for something to eat before long. One way to fight this night-time worrying is to write down all the things that are on your mind and then put the paper aside and those things out of your mind until the morning. If you still can't sleep, don't just lie there, read a book, do a relaxation exercise, or get up and do something practical (NOT EATING).

Night eating is probably the worst aspect of compulsive eating. In the cold dark hours of the night, you feel particularly isolated and vulnerable, and all your problems appear much larger. Sleeping tablets and alcohol are not the answer. These only disguise the symptoms temporarily instead of getting to the root of the problem; they also make it more difficult to fight off the desire to eat by weakening your natural will-power and alcohol actually stimulates the appetite.

Sometimes waking in the night is nothing to do with your own body. Children with nightmares or babies that need feeding upset your natural sleep pattern and can often start off a night eating pattern that continues long after the children are old enough to sleep through the night. If it is just habit to wake up and eat in the night, try locking the kitchen door to help you break the habit.

Seasons of the year

It is usually easier to come to terms with eating problems in the summer. You feel less inclined to eat hot stodgy food when there are plenty of salad foods in the shops, and in the evening it is easier to go out and be active instead of sitting watching television in front of the fire.

January is the worst month of the year for many compulsive eaters. It is cold and dark, Christmas food is still more than a memory, as the extra inches around the waist and hips prove. Like the low days in the month, the same rules apply for the low months of the year. Plan ahead to do something interesting in January, even take a holiday abroad if you can afford it, or arrange a new interesting diet that will include exciting food without extra calories. This is also an excellent time of the year for taking up a new sport, hobby or form of exercise, as all the clubs and classes are in full swing.

There is never a better time than today to start your new eating plan, whether it is dark January, rainy April, sweltering July or depressing November. Don't wait for next Monday morning, after Christmas or when you get back from your summer holidays.

Weekend blues

Weekends are also danger times for the compulsive eater because they often represent a breakdown in normal routine. Going to work each day usually means it is not possible to eat and provides a form of discipline, but at the weekend you are at home with the larder and the refrigerator for company, or out shopping or visiting well-meaning friends and relatives.

The answer is to keep busy at the weekends, if necessary get yourself another part-time job to take your mind off food and get you away from temptations.

Housewives often find they eat more at weekends because they are feeling resentful towards their husband and children. For the family it is a time of freedom and enjoyment, while mum has to work harder than ever cooking and cleaning. When it is not appreciated that Saturday and Sunday are not days off for her, she can become angry and allow resentment to build up which is expressed by binges.

Remember that everybody else is probably as bored and fed up as you at weekends. It is so easy to believe the rest of the world is out there having a marvellous time and you are the only person who is lonely and bored. Tune in to those low spots of the week and plan ahead to fill them with positive actions.

CHAPTER ELEVEN

Feeling Deprived

It is neither the pain nor the place, but only the cause that makes a martyr.

The Church History of Britain, 1665
Thomas Fuller

On the surface bingeing would appear to be the exact opposite of deprivation; the compulsive eater's problem seems to be allowing herself too much rather than too little. But compulsive eating involves much more than over-eating; the fact that the compulsive eater puts too much food into her mouth may well be a way of compensating for the ways in which she is depriving herself, both physically and emotionally.

Food is the great comforter, a solace in times of crisis, unhappiness and overwhelming inability to cope with life. Food is what fills the gap.

Is your body deprived?

Hunger and malnutrition are the major causes of bingeing, so if you try to lose weight by starving yourself, sooner or later your body will rebel against the deprivation you are inflicting on it and compel you to binge. Not eating enough is a sure way to put on weight, because it will lead to binge after binge. This applies to anyone, not just those with eating problems. Any person deprived of sufficient food for a period of time becomes obsessed with the thought of food, even though, previously, they rarely gave it a thought.

In 1945 an experiment was carried out in an American

university by Ancel Keys who asked volunteers, in their mid-twenties, of average height and weight for their age, to follow a strict diet. They were allowed only half of their usual ration of food, and within a few months it became clear that they were all suffering emotionally, and their mental activity had narrowed to thinking about food; meal-times became the focus of their lives. At the end of the test period they had all lost weight. They then gradually began increasing their daily food allowances, but although they ate large amounts, they said they always felt hungry until they reached around the weight they had been before the start of the experiment. And not only did they constantly feel hungry, they also remained miserable and apathetic, only regaining their old personalities when they regained their original weight.

Starvation is *not* the answer to losing weight. A well-balanced, healthy diet is one that gives sufficient calories each day so that your body does not feel deprived, but gradually sheds its extra pounds.

Are you missing out emotionally?

Seeking the comfort of food may mean you are depriving yourself emotionally rather than nutritionally. Do you try to be the ideal wife and mother who puts her family first and feels guilty about having anything for herself? Are you the hard-working secretary who goes without praise or a proper wage for the good of the firm?

It is very much part of being a woman to give to others and take nothing for herself. She buys things for her husband and children, but never for herself. Her children must have the best shoes with the right length and width for growing feet, but her down-at-heel shoes let the water in. Her husband has a big car, business lunches, smart office suits and membership at the golf club; she has a new washing-machine and stays at home all day doing the laundry. She also deprives herself of time, she is always at the beck and call of others. Maybe her mother brought her up to believe that is the way things should be, but deep down she resents the way she is deprived of time to herself.

Exercise

Take half an hour out of each day to do something you really want to do (NOT EATING). Organise your work and responsibilities to fit around it – perhaps get up half an hour earlier in the morning to give yourself a manicure or ask your husband to take the children out for a walk while you read a book by your favourite author. This exercise is only valid if you refuse to FEEL GUILTY about indulging yourself.

Are you depriving yourself intellectually?

The idea that only men or wealthy people should be educated and intellectual is now completely out of date. Everyone has a brain and the opportunity to use it, but for many any kind of intellectual work stops the day they leave school. If you have a boring job, or feel that housework only makes physical, not mental, demands upon you, you should look for something that is intellectually stimulating to do in your free time. If you are stretching your mental abilities sufficiently, you are less likely to think about your eating problems at every available moment.

Have you got fulfilment at work?

Doing a job you dislike is depriving yourself of fulfilment and a sense of satisfaction. There are certain chores that always have to be done, but when the major part of your day and your main occupation is something you really hate, the balance is tipped too far the other way.

JOAN was a headmistress who had a good job, but was unhappy in it. She felt she was always under pressure and disagreed with the teaching system in force at the school. She was a compulsive eater and turned to food because she felt she was not getting any satisfaction from the career she had worked so long and hard to carve out for herself. Finally, she made the decision to change, and now runs her own little business looking after people's houses and pets while they are away on holiday. Other people could not understand why she

100

should give up a career for such a precarious job, but she enjoys her work, fits the hours into the life-style she wants to lead, and is happy. For her it is not a step down because she no longer feels deprived of job satisfaction, and it has helped her overcome her eating problems.

Are you depriving yourself in relationships?

Another common problem among compulsive eaters is that they deprive themselves of fulfilling personal relationships. Take the compulsive eater who has managed to get a boyfriend – at last. Maybe he isn't exactly the man of her dreams, in fact they don't really get on very well at all, but he is better than nothing, so she clings on to him. Not only is she unfulfilled in the relationship, but she is also depriving herself of the opportunity of a better social life and a more satisfactory relationship with someone else.

When ALISON was a teenager at university, she was unable to show any kind of anger, hate or jealousy. Everyone considered her an angel because she went around with a permanent smile on her face. She had a boyfriend who she used to go and visit in his room, but almost every time she went to see him, another girl would be sitting there chatting and taking his attention. Alison would continue to visit him and to sit there with a smile on her face until she could not stand the situation any longer, and she would go back to her room and start eating.

She did not know that she was angry, and she was unable to tell her boyfriend that when she came to see him she did not expect him to have other people there. She needed to work out for herself that she was angry with the girl for being there, with the boyfriend for letting the girl be there, and with herself for putting up with a situation which she found unsatisfactory. She also had to recognise that she was jealous of the other girl, not only because she was friendly with her boyfriend, but also because she seemed so confident and able to cope with life.

In fact, Alison never did come to terms with the situation, and in the end she gave up the boyfriend, depriving herself of the relationship. Possibly she was better off without him, because he seemed a rather unfeeling and not at all caring sort of person; however, she should have said something to him. In the end, the boyfriend was confused and unhappy because he did not understand why Alison had been smiling and friendly one minute, and then broken up with him the next. The girl probably never knew she was in any way involved in the situation, and Alison was alone, bingeing and unhappy in her own room. This was a case of a complete breakdown of communications. Alison was never going to get any better until she learnt to speak up and she would have benefited greatly from attending a self-assertiveness course.

What is deprivation?

If you adore pickled onions and there aren't any in the house you feel deprived, but if you don't like pickles, you don't feel at all deprived because you can't have any. Your attitude and taste determines whether or not you feel deprived, not the presence or lack of the pickled onions.

It is important to get the balance right between deprivation and over-indulgence. If you want to maintain a slim figure, you have got to accept the fact that there are certain foods you cannot eat, or can only eat very occasionally, and with great care. If you feel sacrificing those foods is worth the pleasure of being slim, you will not feel deprived.

When does giving up something become deprivation? This is a personal decision you have to work out for yourself. Starving yourself by only taking in an unreasonably low number of calories is deprivation, but, on the other hand, by over-eating you are depriving yourself of the slim figure you truly desire. The trick is turning that feeling of deprivation around so that it works in your favour instead of leaving you feeling dissatisfied. If you want to be slim and you eat regular meals, including a doughnut with your morning coffee each day, giving up that daily doughnut should not be deprivation unless you choose to make it so in your own mind. Work out your personal priorities and discover what deprivation actually means to you. In certain cases the emotional problems of sacrificing something you really crave may outweigh the benefits of depriving yourself of it.

For example, take the case of Jayne, who phoned the Maisner Centre one day to say she had felt miserable and deprived all week because her interpretation of the eating plan gave her the impression that she could not join the family in their take-away meal of spare ribs and chips. She thought about it all for days, and felt so deprived she had an enormous binge which took in more calories than the spare ribs and chips would have included if she had eaten these in the first place.

There are two points to bear in mind here. One is that, except for health reasons, and the fact that it is a very high-calorie meal, there is no earthly reason why this sort of meal should not be enjoyed on rare occasions; there is, after all, no sugar in this meal. So, put in that situation, enjoy the meal, and adjust your eating intake for the rest of the week to compensate if you are trying to lose weight. But the second point, which is the main point, is what is the real deprivation here? If Jayne's emotional well-being for a whole week depends on spare ribs and chips, it is possible that she has a much deeper problem than a mere love of that particular meal.

Getting the balance right

If you suffer acutely in an emotional way because you feel deprived of food when you are dieting, do you really want to lose that weight? Ask yourself honestly if there is, perhaps, some reason why you prefer to be overweight. It can happen that a woman loses a lot of weight and suddenly becomes young and attractive again, but her husband is so afraid he will lose her to another man that their relationship suffers, and she puts the weight back on again. In this case, her balance sheet says that being slim is not worth an unhappy relationship with the man she loves.

If you really have to starve to get rid of those last few pounds to reach your ideal weight, do you feel the extra effort is depriving you? Ask yourself if it really matters if you are half a stone overweight. And who will notice, apart from yourself? Most husbands are quite unaware of any comparatively minor change in weight on the part of their wives, they just wish they would be happy and content with the weight they are.

If you really feel deprived if you cannot eat large quantities of food whenever you want – cream cakes between meals, and bars of chocolate in the evenings – then yours is not a hunger problem, but a personality one, and you need to find out what is wrong in your life. If the problem is serious, then it may need professional help to sort out your emotional problems.

Exercise
Draw up your own 'balance sheet'. Write down on one side what your aims are, such as your ideal weight, fitness, better relationships, etc. On the other side, list what you feel you have to give up to achieve your goals – not only certain foods, but bad habits and wrong attitudes. From this list pick out anything you think you would feel really deprived of; decide whether that deprivation would be strong enough to spoil the pleasure of achieving your goal, and, if so, try and work out a compromise. You might find your balance sheet looks something like Chart 11.1.

Get to the true reason

Always make sure you are being honest with yourself about your reasons for feeling deprived. If you say, 'I can't go to the pictures because everyone else will be eating ice cream and I shall feel deprived', are you really going to feel deprived of ice cream (take an apple with you if you need to eat something), or is it more that you will feel deprived because it is not the film you want to see, because you will be on your own and everyone else will be in couples, because everyone else you know is doing something more interesting than going to the pictures?

There is no need to feel deprived if you go out for a meal in a restaurant and everyone else is eating cream gateau. Deprivation is very much an attitude of mind in such a situation; keep concentrating on how virtuous you are in not having a sweet, and how it will help you maintain your figure (remember the balance sheet). If you have a firm aim in view, sacrifice is not a deprivation.

Be nice to others

Don't deprive everyone else just because you feel deprived. Just because you are suffering, there is no need to make everyone else miserable, and just because you are on a diet, there is no need for the rest of the family to starve. If they insist on apple pie and cream, cook the apple first and keep some aside for yourself before making the pie. You won't feel deprived of a sweet, and they can still have what they want.

Nobody likes living with a martyr, so don't keep telling the children how many sacrifices you are making for them, what you have to go without to bring them up. They will only be resentful and create a bad atmosphere in the house which will upset you, and of course lead to bingeing.

Count your blessings

In spite of what the media and the advertising men would have us believe, nobody can have everything in life. Maybe you have got enough money to live comfortably, but you are on your own, or perhaps you really have to struggle to make ends meet, but at least you have a good husband. For most people, life is a matter of balancing out the good and the bad, but it is always easier to worry and fret over the problems, ignoring the good things, than to be grateful for what you have.

Exercise
Write down a list of ten things that you have got which your neighbour/colleague/sister, etc, has not (for example, an ambition to overcome your eating problem). These must all be positive things, good things which are in your life but missing

Chart 11.1 A sample 'balance sheet'

	Debit	Credit	Balance
MONDAY	I just can't resist the chocolate I've bought for the kids today.	Of course I can. I'll have an apple to take my mind off it.	Felt virtuous and in control.
TUESDAY	I feel so lethargic. The TV is boring. Maybe I'll binge tonight and start afresh tomorrow.	No, I won't. I'll ring my friend and see if she wants to come to an aerobics class.	Feeling physically toned up and learning to take the initiative with friends.
WEDNESDAY	Damned office parties. I'd love to have a good few drinks to help me relax.	But booze always makes me binge. I should know by now that even one drink sets me off, so I won't bother.	Had no hangover the next day. Increase in confidence after realising I can cope with a social function without 'dutch courage'.
THURSDAY	Mum always insists I eat when I call in to see her. Today she's just baked a cake. I'll have to eat a slice to keep her quiet.	Why should I please her at such an expense to myself. I don't want sugary things anymore. I'll ask her for an apple.	Felt proud about being assertive with my mother and was left feeling no resentment towards her for a change.
FRIDAY	'He's going out again tonight. As I've been so good all week, I think I'll treat myself to some goodies as I have to spend the evening alone.	On the other hand I could easily get the girl downstairs to babysit and go out with my sister instead. We haven't had a good chinwag in months.	Husband is happier I'm getting out and about a bit more. We have more to talk about.
SATURDAY	Children are so wasteful! Look at this food they've left. Maybe I'll eat it. I can't bear to throw it away.	But I also can't afford to pick in between meals. I'll end up bingeing. I'll save a tin of dog food and give it to the dog for dinner.	Self-respect growing. I am no longer a human dustbin.

	Debit	*Credit*	*Balance*
SUNDAY	I really don't feel like going to my in-laws all day today. I'm going to have a sandwich while I think of an excuse to back out. I've got so much to do today.	Instead of eating that sandwich, I'll ring my in-laws and suggest we only go for the afternoon today. It will give me time for chores this morning and time for myself this evening. They will just have to understand I am pushed for time today.	Learning not to procrastinate because this leads to bingeing. My self-esteem is growing.

Total credit balance

2 pounds lighter in weight
More control of my life in general, but most important with food
Better relations with husband and others
Confidence increasing
Assertiveness increasing
Resentment towards others decreasing and in turn general frustration with myself and others is less
Self-esteem growing
Learning to respect myself more
Learning not to put off what can be dealt with now
Much less depressed
More energy and enthusiasm generally

from other people's, even though they appear not to lack anything. If you cannot immediately list ten things, leave the paper and pen handy, and keep adding things as they occur to you until you reach ten. If you still cannot write down ten things, try asking someone else what they think you have that they lack. You may be amazed at the things other people envy you for that you take completely for granted.

CHAPTER TWELVE

Coming to Terms with Negative Emotions

I was angry with my friend,
I told my wrath, my wrath did end.
I was angry with my foe,
I told it not, my wrath did grow.
William Blake

Thoughts are the shapes on which a character is built, but emotions are the colours that bring it to life. Emotions influence the decisions we make and through emotions we express how we feel towards others. Relationships are built on this two-way exchange of love, hate, anger, jealousy, desire.

Emotion is the positive force which inspires decisions, changes the course of a person's life, and brings them to maturity. But every emotion has its positive and its negative side, depending from which angle it is viewed. If a man loses his job at the age of 50 he can see it as the end of his life and sink into despair and old age, or he can collect his golden handshake and start again on a different career.

It is never too late to make a new start, to lose weight, to get eating under control, to replace an obsession with food with an interest in other things in life. In fact once positive steps have been made to start a new life most people find they make a much better job of it the second time round.

When faced with problems and difficulties in life, different people react in different ways. Some might turn to drink, others become violent or suicidal, others develop physical symptoms such as ulcers. Nobody really understands why different people react to life in different ways. The compulsive eater turns to food in times of distress, which is perhaps the most obvious direction because most of us are brought up to associate food with being comforted.

It does not take long for the infant to begin to associate displays of emotion with milk or a dummy in the mouth, followed throughout childhood by a promise of sweets if he does not cry, and an ice cream if he does as he is told. Food is the first comfort we get in our lives and for many it remains the easiest thing to turn to in times of emotional crisis.

To overcome the compulsion to turn to food it is necessary to reverse the pattern of thought and turn negative into positive. Admit you are angry with yourself for bingeing and express that anger. Learn to revel in the challenge of beating your habit instead of giving up in despair at the thought of the long, weary fight. Stand up and tell yourself, 'I am a compulsive eater.' Once you have admitted you have this problem you have a reason to justify each backward step during your journey to controlling it, and there will be no need to feel guilty.

Expressing emotions outwards into the world is a positive attitude, but if they are turned inward on the self, they take on a negative role. If you ask compulsive eaters whether or not they find it difficult to be angry and aggressive when their rights and privileges are threatened, almost without exception they will reply that they do, or that they can only show anger in the security of their family unit.

Any emotion that is suppressed and working against the best interests of the person experiencing it can be called a negative emotion. This chapter deals with the most obvious ones.

Anger

Anger expressed openly towards the person or object that is causing it is a positive form of emotion, but it can be turned inwards and become anger at self or simmer and boil beneath a calm exterior. It can also be misdirected and rebound on an innocent party.

If a child is crossing the road and nearly gets knocked down, it is a common reaction for the mother to be angry with the child as a way of expressing her relief that he is safe, even if it was the car driver who was at fault. A man under a lot of pressure at the office comes home and rages and storms at his wife all evening.

Misdirected anger leads to bad feeling within families, so it is important to work out who or what is the real reason for that anger and direct the emotion positively in that direction. Don't kick the cat because you have just eaten a packet of biscuits.

Women are expected to be good listeners, to bear the brunt of other people's frustrations without having any of their own. To conform to this role many women, particularly if they are wives and mothers, feel guilty if they take their anger out on their families, so they bottle up their feelings or become angry with themselves for misdirecting their anger.

BRIDGET had a regular visitor who always chain smoked her cigarettes and never offered to smoke his own. After a year she still had not said anything to him about this. She was unable to say no, so she could not tell him to go and buy his own cigarettes even though she was seething with indignation at his behaviour. Every time he helped himself to another cigarette she would make an excuse to go out to the kitchen to get herself something to eat, then after he had gone she would go on a binge. At a workshop Bridget told the others about her problem and a role playing session was set up. A third person took the role of the visitor and Bridget told him all about her indignation at his behaviour. She was able to analyse her feelings and discover that she was angry with him for taking her cigarettes and angry with herself for letting him. It also became obvious that as he had been smoking her cigarettes for a year and she had never said a word or showed she minded, he did not realise that she was being upset by his behaviour. Next time he came to visit her she told him she was upset by his behaviour. She told him he could not smoke her cigarettes, so he went down to the shop and bought a packet for himself which he shared with her.

Resentment

Bottled-up anger often leads to resentment and people can brood over real or imaginary grievances for years. It is often difficult to show resentment without the risk of upsetting someone, and this is a situation compulsive eaters always try to avoid. Small things can grow huge and out of proportion if brooded on for long periods, like the mother who resented the fact that she made puddings for the rest of the family, but could not eat them herself because of the calories. In this case it was pointed out to her that it was possible to have low-calorie desserts; for example, she could have stewed apple while the others ate apple pie and cream.

Women yearn to be loved and will sacrifice pride and all personal ambition to please their husband and children, but grow resentful if they just take her for granted and fail to appreciate her sacrifices. Asking others for help is not a sign of failure, but having to receive help can often lead to resentment.

SAMANTHA, as part-time secretary in a school, appeared to the world as a highly composed person, but because she was a compulsive eater she went along to a workshop and there she was asked to tell her group something she had never told anyone before. The great secret that she had been choking back since she was young was that she had been unable to tell her father she did not want to vote Conservative.

It may seem a small thing, but for years that resentment had been burning inside Samantha and helping to push her down the path of compulsive eating. She felt angry at herself for not standing up to her father, and resentful of him for not allowing her to hold her own political views. She was unable to confront him with her beliefs for fear of upsetting him.

As a result of talking about this deep-seated resentment, Samantha learnt to cry. She had not cried for twenty years and this emotional breakdown of her composed exterior opened the gates for much more emotion to be released and put her on the road to controlling her eating problems.

Guilt

From early childhood our standards of behaviour are given to us by other people and we accept these standards without stopping to question whether they are necessarily right or not. Children assume that what their parents and teachers tell them is right, until in later life they find things are not quite as they have always thought them. It is easy to feel guilty about trusting one's own judgement and going against what figures of authority have taught us. Children don't recognise this as guilt. To them it is a striving to please and to attain an acceptable pattern of behaviour. Adults with a very strict code of thought can inflict impossible standards on their children which will load them with guilt throughout their lives, and even the most well-meaning parents can be unaware of how the way they live their lives and the things they say are affecting their children.

For example, a little girl of five was always being told by her parents, 'You'll be the death of me.' One day she went to play in the park when she knew her parents would not approve and when she came back her father had died of a heart attack. At that age she believed her naughtiness had been the death of her father and for many years she carried a deep sense of guilt for his death.

Guilt can be nurtured by too much absorption in self and too great a willingness to blame oneself for all the troubles in the world. How big is your load of guilt? As an exercise try answering these questions and then write down all the things you feel guilty about.

1 Do I have the right to have half an hour to myself each day?
2 Do I have the right to cook something I like as opposed to meals the family like?
3 Do I have the right to be treated as a person?
4 Do I have the right to pamper myself?
5 Do I have the right to ask anybody else to help me?

If your answer to any of these was, 'Yes, I do have the right', then go ahead and do it without feeling guilty. If you answered,

'No' to all of them because they would make you feel guilty, try and work out the reasons behind such a huge load of guilt. Do you in fact enjoy feeling guilty? Choose one of the above and resolve to do it anyway. If you really have these feelings of guilt, ask your doctor to refer you to a psychotherapist for help.

It is common for anyone with an eating problem to feel guilty about eating. For example, you set yourself a calorie limit of 1,000 calories then exceed it by 100 calories, feel guilty, so carry on eating. You are determined not to eat biscuits, but you have one and feel so guilty you finish off the packet. Eating one or two biscuits is not a thing to feel guilty about, all sorts of people do it all the time. Whatever the reason that led you to eat that first biscuit, it is likely to be guilt that will be responsible for you eating the rest.

If you find yourself on an eating binge in the morning, come to terms with the fact that you have done it, that you have suffered a temporary setback because you are a compulsive eater. Let that be the end of the matter and find a way to express the anger you feel with yourself. Once you allow yourself to feel guilty about that morning binge it will drag out and you will continue eating all day.

Jealousy

Jealousy often has its roots in childhood, starting with jealous feelings towards a brother or sister who appears to be cleverer, better looking or more loved. In later life this jealousy takes the form of seeing everybody else as perfect and only yourself as having faults. Some of the most common cries found as an expression of jealousy are, 'Everyone else has a perfect figure', or if they are overweight, 'It doesn't matter because they look good in their clothes.' In fact people who always look good are usually the ones who spend a lot of time and effort working on themselves. They follow diets, exercise, go to the hairdresser, have a strict beauty routine, and they feel good about themselves. They have earned the right to look good.

'Other people never seem to have problems': there is nobody in the world who does not have problems, but with maturity comes the ability to keep problems in proportion and not let them take over. How many people know about your problems? You probably appear to them as someone without a care in the world. Learn to see people as they really are and not as they appear superficially.

'Everybody else has more money than me': there are not many really rich people around these days. Those who seem to have money to throw about are probably extravagant and living beyond their means or making economies in other directions. They are probably worried about their financial situation and may be using money as a way of compensating for their feelings of inferiority. How much money are you spending on eating binges?

One of the best ways to deal with jealousy is to play other people at their own game. Look honestly at yourself and decide which is your best feature. Everybody has something they can be proud of, perhaps their eyes or their hands, and work on this to make the most of it so that others will be jealous of you. There is probably someone who envies you already, for example, most working women envy those that stay at home all day, and most housewives envy the career woman. If there is someone who does not appear to like you for no obvious reason, consider carefully if they are perhaps jealous of you. Jealousy is a common emotion.

Hate

Hate can be the most powerful of the negative emotions, but real hate is something that is rarely found. If you think you hate a particular person or thing, analyse the feeling carefully to see if it is really something else. If you say you hate dogs, perhaps you are really frightened of them. If you think you hate your sister, is it jealousy that you truly feel, or does she intimidate you or just bore you?

Getting to the root of the feeling is a help in sorting out the reasons behind it and how to come to terms with it. Not understanding a person or a situation is often at the root of a hatred.

Depression

Depression is the ultimate negative state. The path of depression leads a person further and further into themselves until they become obsessed with themselves and cut off from the world. Nobody has the real cure for depression, because for each individual the answer only exists within themselves. A good night's sleep, a balanced diet and going out and doing something fulfilling is the most simplified answer to the problem.

There is such a thing as clinical depression which needs medical treatment. The sufferer has no real reason to feel depressed in this case, but if you are a compulsive eater this is reason enough for depression, so try this plan for a month and see if you begin to feel better.

The plan gives something to do each day, something to do each week, and something to do each month. Make a commitment and write down the day and time you are going to perform the chosen act. When that time comes you must do it, there can be no exceptions and no excuses. Keep a timetable to monitor how you are doing and mark with a tick every time you do the thing you have committed yourself to.

The idea is to re-awaken awareness of the person and feelings you have learnt to ignore. Learn to take responsibility for your own pleasures, rather than demanding them from other people. A compulsive eater concentrates so much on food and her eating problem that she forgets she has other features in her life such as a good brain, a lovely home.

The anti-depression plan

EACH DAY

1.   Smile and talk to someone and pay them a compliment, for example, the postman, a shop assistant or the bus conductor.
2.   Say NO to someone or something. But this does not necessarily mean food, it can be anything you don't want to do.

EACH WEEK

1.   Read a non-fiction book on a subject you know nothing about.

2.   Tell someone about your compulsive eating and if possible ask them to help you, or if you are always going on about it, don't talk about it for a week.

3.   Do something to help a member of your family or a friend: for example, babysit or do the washing up.

4.   Do a job which you have been promising yourself for a long time: for example, write an outstanding letter, catch up with the mending or telephone that friend.

5.   Buy yourself something new, even if it is just a bottle of nail varnish.

6.   Go out of your way to be pleasant to someone who has been unpleasant to you or someone you simply don't like.

7.   Change something in your appearance, for example, put your hair up, varnish your nails if you don't usually use nail varnish. Don't just wait until you are 'the right shape'; you never will be until you have sorted out your problems.

8.   If there is nothing of interest on the television, turn it off and do something else: for instance, read that non-fiction book, or do something creative.

9.   Do something you used to enjoy doing before your eating problems appeared and you felt depressed.

EACH MONTH

1.   Take up a new hobby or interest: for example, join an evening class.

Remember that if depression fills a large part of your life, removing it will leave a void, so organise something to fill the gap. Aim to replace depression rather than just cut it out of your life, or you will probably fail and the chain of new emotions that experience sparks off will make the situation worse than ever.

A smile is the easiest first step to reverse the negative trend of depression. There is nothing that lifts the spirits like a smile, so try forcing your face into a grin and see if that does not immediately lighten the load a bit. The image you send out into the world is the image you will receive back, so giving a positive sign, like a smile to someone, will bring back a positive response. A depressed person makes other people's lives a misery too and they tend to avoid them, while a sunny generous personality is always the centre of attention. There is great truth in the biblical saying, 'As you sow, so shall you reap', and it is up to you to make the first positive move.

Fear

Fear is the emotion that is usually the excuse for not facing up to realities. Analyse your fear and see if it is really a cover up for something else. Think back and discover what that fear stems from; was it something that was comforted by food when you were a little child?

A little girl went to the toilet and the chain broke, but when she stood on the seat to mend it a huge moth startled her and she fell into the toilet. From then on she was frightened of the moth, but her mother said she could not have anything to eat if she did not go to the toilet, so she had to overcome her fear of the moth. Later in life, when she became a compulsive eater, every time she had to overcome a fear of anything, it became associated with food.

It is easy for little things to get blown up out of proportion, and it is often small fears that set off an eating binge rather than really big terrifying experiences. A common fear is what will a husband or boyfriend say if he finds out about your compulsive eating habits. Those who have undertaken treatment and faced up to this problem have discovered in many cases that he already knew, and nobody has ever lost a husband when he was told.

As well as being obsessed with food the compulsive eater also has a great fear of food because she knows what a powerful influence it has over her. She knows she cannot control her eating and lives in constant fear of the next binge. The only way to beat fear is to face up to it. Accept that the next binge will come and it is all part of the process of getting better. Be prepared for it, which is not the same as being frightened of it, and realise that the more you worry about it the more likely it is to happen.

It is too easy to slip into the habit of exaggerating all the negative things in your life and brushing aside the positive. In this way things get out of proportion and appear so much more difficult and gloomy than they really are.

JANET had an overwhelming desire for chocolate biscuits so she got in the car and drove to the shop to get some. When she got to the shop she picked up the packet, then put it down and bought some fruit instead. Afterwards she could only dwell on the negative aspect of how she had craved those biscuits instead of rejoicing at the positive side which was that, when it came to the crunch, she was actually able to stop herself and choose fruit instead. For someone battling against eating problems this was a major victory.

Don't let the positive things drown in an ocean of negative thoughts and emotions. Nurture and encourage every little positive thing in your life and they will gradually grow and grow until you find your whole attitude to life has shifted to something far more constructive and satisfying. It is a knack to be able to refocus your vision of an event to see the positive instead of the negative, like looking at one of those optical illusion pictures that can look like a silhouette of a beautiful woman or of an ugly old crone depending on how you perceive it. Life is much the same. It's odd but if you start taking a better view of things, suddenly everyone else seems a lot nicer as well, proving the old saying, 'Laugh and the world laughs with you, weep and you weep alone.'

CHAPTER THIRTEEN

Taking a Positive Approach

They can because they think they can.
Virgil

Keeping a stiff upper lip was once considered the Great British Virtue, but modern thinking is more enlightened about the dangers of suppressing feelings and emotions. Remember the story of the Spartan boy caught with a wild fox cub: rather than let his teacher know he had the fox he stuffed it inside his tunic and continued talking while the animal gnawed at his stomach. People do much the same thing today, they talk and smile while some excruciating pain is eating away at them inside. This is particularly true amongst those with eating problems.

Although the surface is calm, underneath the spring of emotion is so tightly wound that even a small incident can start off an eating binge. Friends and even family are unaware of a fierce anger and resentment boiling beneath a mild, obliging façade.

It is said that man's greatest desire is to love and be loved. The less we love ourselves the more we crave for others to love us, to the extent of doing almost anything to win affection. Based on early lessons of pleasing parents by not screaming with anger, the next step is to win the love of everyone by not showing emotion. Learning to hold back emotion is another of the lessons learnt in early childhood. Babies scream when they are angry, bored or frustrated, but because adults can't cope with this naked display of feeling they encourage the child not to cry, not to throw a tantrum in the street, not to fling its dinner plate on the floor.

It takes a lot of self-assertion for a child to continue to display anger, rage, jealousy and other anti-social emotions with any great vigour in the face of continual smothering by adults. Most children want to please their parents and so they curb behaviour that distresses them.

The suppression of emotions from earliest childhood has pushed those feelings deep down and bottled them up, with food as the stopper in the bottle. Convinced others won't like them if they show anger or jealousy the compulsive eater only allows that bottle of emotion to be prised open in private and during an eating binge. Putting food in the mouth is the negative expression of emotions that cannot be let out in a positive way.

Workshop technique

Negative emotions are due to a breakdown in communications both with self and others, or a lack of understanding. At the workshops designed to help compulsive eaters come to terms with their problems, much emphasis is put on the importance of communication and on encouraging people to express themselves openly in front of others. One exercise has people standing in groups; one person says, 'I love you' and another says, 'I hate you'. It is very difficult for people to say, 'I hate you' with conviction, their instinct is to avoid giving offence at all costs. Positively seeking love is acceptable, but the negative side of expressing dislike is painful and difficult. Breaking down the barriers can be very traumatic for everyone involved.

If actually confronting the person who is causing your anger and resentment is too much of an ordeal to begin with, try using a substitute. Make sure you are alone in the house and cannot be overheard or interrupted, then get a cushion and tell it everything you want to say about the things you are angry about. Sit and talk sensibly to your cushion or shout at it, kick it and punch it to let out all that anger and resentment. Anything to redirect those emotions outwards instead of inwards. This may be very difficult to begin with, but once you have done it a few times it becomes easier.

Don't expect this to bring an instant answer. It may well bring immediate relief, but it is not easy to face up to a lifetime of emotions as they come to the surface. You may become extremely emotional and there will be some nasty relapses, probably in the second and third week. The confusion and emotion will probably lead to more food as a form of comfort. Don't let such relapses turn inward in the form of guilt and a sense of failure, and don't use such occasions as an easy excuse to give up.

Stop and think

At the moment when you feel you are about to start eating, stop, reflect on why you are doing it. If you realise it is because of some emotional crisis, sit down and explain it all to your cushion, be honest and tell everything. Once in the habit of bringing out suppressed feelings you may feel more able to approach the actual person involved. Often writing a letter to them is easier than talking face to face.

Taking a positive attitude is pushing out feelings into the world and coping with the opposition they may stir up. A negative attitude is the easy option. If you don't show anger and resentment, you will not have to deal with arguments and confrontations. But in the long-term it is the hardest path because instead of fighting the world, the negative person ends up fighting herself. The compulsive eater finds herself caught up in an eating binge at times of crisis whether it is agreeing to sex when she doesn't want it or just smiling at someone who is being rude and hurtful.

Because of this inability to show the appropriate emotion, others usually do not realise what is going on and so are unlikely to change their attitude or make allowances. And so it goes on, with the compulsive eater backing herself further and further into a corner. Not only is she angry at others for the way they treat her, but she is resentful because they do not understand how she is feeling and angry with herself for not being able to tell them how she feels.

JANE offers to look after her neighbour's children. She is pleasant and smiling and appears not to mind, so her neighbour asks her again and again and she always says yes. Inside she is becoming angry and resentful at being imposed upon in this way. She is angry at the neighbour for making continual demands, and angry at herself for not being able to refuse her neighbour's requests. She may or may not realise that her neighbour would not ask her to look after the children if she was aware of the resentment it was causing, but she desperately wants her neighbour to like her and she has never learnt to say no.

In this case Jane told a third person about the situation and used her to play out the scene she had gone over so many times in her own mind. The third person takes the role of the neighbour and the woman said all the things to her that she had been wanting to say to her neighbour.

If you want to try this method and feel you have not got anyone you can ask to play the role of the third person, try using a tape recorder and say everything you want into the machine, then play it back and listen to yourself. If you do not have anyone you feel you can confide in, it is also advisable to read the chapter in this book on loneliness.

The easy option

Lack of self-assertion, like compulsive eating, is particularly common among women. They grow up with such expressions as, 'Nice girls don't ...', and unlike their brothers they can't work off aggression by getting into fights or playing energetic games of football. Self-confidence comes with maturity, but the compulsive eater usually has not achieved either. For some it is convenient to be bulimic, they almost enjoy it: it is the easy negative option. But most people don't see the association between food and emotion until it is pointed out to them.

We are all creatures of habit and anything can become a habit if we do it often enough, even being comforted with sweets instead of being loved and kissed. Recognising these familiar habits and seeing them for what they are is the first stage, then it is possible to notice how often eating binges occur simultaneously with emotional crises. Keeping a careful chart will show this up. Realising that eating binges can be triggered by negative emotions is half-way to controlling them. Awareness can bring about the positive step of trying to express things instead of keeping them hidden.

If something your husband or partner does or does not do is making you feel angry and resentful, find time to sit down and have a long talk with him. Let him know how you feel and you may be surprised how completely unaware he is of how it is affecting you, and also how willing he is to make changes once he realises it is pushing you into eating binges.

JOAN was the secretary who offered to clean the office one Friday before she went home, to please her boss. Somehow it became the accepted routine that every Friday she would stay behind and tidy up. She never said anything and her boss never gave the matter another thought. But she was so indignant at having to do this menial task that each Friday she would go home and binge to work off her anger.

Eventually she sat down and reasoned out for herself that it wasn't her job to do the cleaning and that she must say something to her boss. She spoke to him about it and he was amazed that she was actually still staying behind every Friday night and immediately told her not to do it any more. This was not a cure to her compulsive eating, but it stopped her Friday night binges so her weekends were better and she felt good. This was a first step forward for her, but if she had been able to talk to her boss sooner she would have saved herself months of agonising and bingeing.

Other people are not good at reading your mind, especially if you are making a great effort to hide things from them. You will be surprised time and again how well people react once they know what is in your mind and how you are feeling. It is unlikely they will cease to like you, as the compulsive eater so dreads, and may even like you more once they feel they are getting to know the 'real' you. There is no short cut to changing the habits of a lifetime, but to come to terms with the problems of compulsive eating it is essential to learn to stand up for yourself and not let people push you around.

WENDY stuck to the eating plan except when she felt she had to please other people by eating. She did not really want to eat on any of the occasions, but lacked the ability to stand up for herself and say no. This was a personality problem rather than an eating problem, but it led to her being a compulsive eater. In just one week of filling in charts for the eating plan she recorded:

A cream cake ... 'because mum had bought it and I didn't like to hurt her feelings.' An extra meal ... 'because mum had made it and I didn't like to make a fuss, especially when dad said, "not another diet".'

An unsuitable meal out with her boyfriend ... 'because he wouldn't let me have a salad, he said it wasn't worth buying.'

An Indian meal ... 'because my boyfriend hadn't eaten all day and he didn't want to eat alone so he ordered it for me.'

Excuses, excuses

People talk endlessly about what they are going to do and the changes they are going to make. Take the plunge and actually do that thing, and you will find it is not nearly so difficult as you thought it would be. You keep saying you will go to an evening class, but make all sorts of excuses because the true reason is you lack the self-confidence. See those excuses in their true light and analyse the real reason why you don't sign up for that class. Here are a few of the most popular excuses.

'I can't afford it': but how much will it cost you to stay at home nursing your negative emotions and bingeing on food? What do you spend your money on? Are you, in fact, committing too much to things you think will make you happy which are just causing you misery? For example, is your mortgage too high, might you be more content moving to a smaller house that puts you under less of a financial burden, or are you too deeply committed to hire purchase agreements for possessions you do not really want? Your standard of living should be pitched at a level you can afford, not one that makes you binge through money worries.

'I'm too tired': it is a well-known fact that the less you do the less

you want to do, and the reverse is true. If you want something done, find a busy person to do it. If you find something that interests you your tiredness will evaporate. Keeping busy is good therapy, but it must be kept within reason. Don't set yourself impossible tasks, or you will be angry with yourself when you fail.

'*I can't leave the children*': get together with another parent, and take it in turns to sit with each other's children. Alternatively, it is not difficult to find a student or pensioner willing to babysit once a week.

'*My husband won't like it*': he may sulk for the first couple of weeks, but it is important to explain to him how much it means to you. He probably does not like you sitting at home feeling miserable, and will appreciate your doing something that brings you happiness and contentment. If he is so insecure and jealous that he cannot bear you to go out of the house, that is his problem that he must deal with himself. You must learn to stand up for yourself.

'*I haven't got time*': if you really want to do it, you will find the time. If you spend all day cleaning the house from top to bottom, are you doing it because you find housework fulfilling and satisfying, or from a sense of guilt, or because your mother always kept her home beautiful? Perhaps you are making unnecessary work for yourself, or are just badly organised so it takes you much too long to get through your work. Take a close look at your daily routine. Never having time for yourself is the source of a lot of anger and resentment. Are you so busy trying to please others that you are constantly running around after them from morning to night? They have got into the habit of expecting you to do everything for them. Learn to say no sometimes. How many hours did you spend watching television last week?

Negative to positive

Negative thoughts are the great enemy of all motivations and good intentions. It is very easy to slip into the habit of negative thinking, so it is important to catch yourself every time a negative thought enters your head, and immediately try and think of the positive side. Write them down, if possible; that always helps reinforce the power of your thoughts.

For example:

Negative thought	*Positive statement*
Exercise is boring.	I feel good after exercising.
Buying a packet of doughnuts is easier than cooking a meal.	Only good nutrition and well-balanced meals will correct my eating habits.
I've already eaten more than I had planned, so I might as well carry on.	I have eaten a little extra, but there is no reason to make it a full-scale binge. I can stop now.

Writing notes to yourself and putting them up wherever you are likely to need them is a positive motivation. Notes such as, 'Are you really hungry?' on the larder door, and 'I don't need to eat more than is necessary' on the refrigerator, or 'Today, I am going to eat sensibly' on your dressing-table mirror. Even if you do not always act on the good advice of your notes each time you read them, the message is being repeated to your mind over and over.

Filling in the food charts, as shown in this book, is a daily exercise that helps to boost motivation. All these little tricks help to top up your reserves of motivation as you go through the day and the week. Always remember, laughter is the best medicine; learn to laugh at yourself and your frustrating situations, and life becomes much easier.

Extending the idea

Once you begin to think about what is motivating your life, there is no need to restrict motivation to your eating habits. Your eating problems are not isolated from the rest of your life, they are a sum total of everything you do each day, so improving other areas of your life will also improve your eating habits.

For example: if you work in a shop, set yourself a target of making one extra sale each day that you would not normally have made. If you are a housewife, organise yourself to get your housework done half an hour quicker each day and spend the time you save doing something creative, practical or self-indulgent (but NOT eating).

In everything you do, set yourself a level of achievement that you think you can manage, but without attempting something over-ambitious, which will mean failure, followed by frustration and guilt. Stretching your ability a little each day not only boosts self-esteem and brings self-satisfaction, but also occupies you that little bit more so you have less opportunity to think about eating.

What's holding you back?

If by now you have worked out what things are likely to motivate you to achieve what you set your mind on, are you also aware what things are motivating you to carry on eating in spite of your good resolutions? Refer to the mood section of your weekly chart and when you see a pattern emerging at the end of the week, read the appropriate chapters in this book to help come to grips with your particular problems.

So there it is, the thing that motivates you to eat. What are you going to do about it? This is something that needs thinking about clearly and logically. Before you can start making changes, you have got to sort out exactly what you are trying to achieve; in other words – you can't cook the lunch before you have washed up the breakfast dishes.

Exercise
Get a kitchen timer, pencil and paper. Write down what you think your biggest motivation for eating is, for example, 'angry with husband', then set your timer to go off after five minutes, extending the time as you continue the exercise each day.

Until that bell rings, you are not going to think about anything else except what you have written on your paper. At first, you will find it difficult to keep your mind from wandering, even for five minutes, but if you find yourself getting sidetracked into worrying about your finances, or your figure, gently direct your mind back to what you have written on your paper. Do not allow yourself to think about food. Tell yourself you can think about everything else after the bell rings.

This is not an excuse to WALLOW IN SELF-PITY, but a set time to think clearly and logically about one subject. Don't try to come to an instant solution or work out any answers; just look at your problems as if you were an outsider. The answer to your problem is already there inside you, but you are making so much commotion worrying about your problems that you are unable to hear the still little voice of reason within you. Training yourself to have periods of quiet thought will, in time, allow this voice to be heard, and answers will begin to come through.

When the bell on the timer rings, your thinking period is over and you are not going to give that subject any more conscious thought for the rest of the day. However, it is important to repeat this exercise every day.

CHAPTER FOURTEEN

Regaining Self-confidence

Confidence is a plant of slow growth.
Earl of Chatham

Lack of confidence is a lot more widespread in society than many people realise. Scratch just beneath the surface of even the most outgoing and self-assured individual and a whole array of uncertainties, fears and self-doubts will come quickly to light.

Most people do a good job at covering up their lack of confidence, either by brazening it out in an aggressive way or by going to great lengths to avoid situations in which they will be put to the test. So when you feel shy in the presence of those who appear to be swanning along through life, the chances are they are all fighting their own secret battles.

A situation which one person can take in their stride is fraught with anxieties for another, while in a different situation the tables may be reversed. For example, a man who is the life and soul of the pub may feel out of his depth in a one to one situation, while the man who is at ease at home with his wife suffers agonies of shyness at a cocktail party.

Few people are totally at ease in every situation, so most people plan their lives to centre around the things they feel comfortable doing and avoid situations where they are out of their depth. Problems arise where a person feels unable to face almost any situation, or insists on driving herself into areas to which she is not suited. This leads to inner tension and, in the case of the compulsive eater, the inevitable bingeing to compensate. Those who lack confidence to such an extent that it drastically restricts their life can usually trace this back to childhood and upbringing.

CAROLE is a career girl aged 27. She has a high-powered job which is really more than she can cope with, but she refuses to give it up because that would mean admitting defeat. She has no time for boyfriends. That was an area in which she felt unsure of herself so she spent every hour of the day at her job in which she knew she could be successful. She says she feels like a working and eating machine and she will think about finding a boyfriend when she has got over her eating problem.

Eating is Carole's way of giving herself love, but she needs to learn to love herself before she can feel happy in a relationship with someone else. Her crisis of identity comes from not seeing herself as a person. Her only experience of men has been brief encounters with no commitments, as soon as it begins to develop into a deeper relationship, she begins to withdraw.

It can start in childhood

Domineering parents, however well meaning, who force their children to attempt things they do not feel able to cope with, and criticise them for not doing well, are sowing the seeds for lack of confidence in adult life. Parents of a shy child may bribe her with food to go out and meet people: 'If you come to grandma's, she will give you a chocolate biscuit'; 'if you come shopping with me, I will buy you a packet of crisps'. These are early introductions to associating food with being forced into uncomfortable social situations. A child is sent to spend the holidays with her aunt, but she is quiet and shy and not used to speaking up, so she feels dull beside her lively talkative cousins. She is fat and cannot keep up with them, so they soon get tired of her and begin to ignore her. Throughout her life she will carry the feeling of being the 'poor relation'.

Parents often have high expectations of their children and in most families there is a favourite to whom the other is constantly compared. 'Why can't you be more like your brother' is a phrase guaranteed to foster discord in a family and warp the child who comes to believe he can do nothing right in his parents' eyes. He may become aggressive or he may give up and slip comfortably into the role of second best that his parents have created for him, growing up without the confidence and self-esteem to follow up his full potential. Because parents often have a fixed idea of how they want their children to be, they do not accept the fact that one child may have a different view of life.

A child whose school marks are average might have the approval of her parents if her sister was not always top of her class and they are continually being compared. If the parents become so obsessed with lack of academic achievement, they won't notice that the less bright child excels her sister in other ways, perhaps she has a less selfish nature or a greater ability for hard work than the sister to whom everything in life comes easily.

When confidence is shaken

A traumatic experience can bring about a sudden lack of confidence in someone who has never been aware of the problem before. Eating problems can suddenly flare up after a shock that shakes a person's confidence, such as divorce or redundancy. A woman has her life neatly sorted out. She runs her home efficiently, cares for her children and perhaps has a part-time job to help pay the bills. She feels secure in her routine and her life is arranged so that there is no need for her to take on challenges that test her too strongly.

Out of the blue her husband announces he is leaving her. He feels stifled in the narrow domestic world she has created for the family and he feels hurt because in her well-organised world she has failed to notice he is not happy. For the first time in many years she finds herself alone and having to face many new problems. She feels bitter against her husband, probably pursuing him through the courts for every penny she can squeeze out of him, but nothing can bring back the confidence she once felt when she was secure in her domestic world.

Food is a tranquilliser when facing difficulties and situations where confidence may be lacking. It is much easier to eat something and so put off the time when it is necessary to face the moment of truth. This is a very common situation and one familiar even to those without eating problems, another cup of coffee before going in to face the boss, one more cigarette before the driving test. Only with the compulsive eater the situation is exaggerated into a massive binge that takes the place of going for a job interview or a date with a boyfriend. If a woman wakes in the morning feeling fat, her confidence to face the day disappears and she begins to eat, knowing the binge will probably last all day. She despairs and reaches for food as a comforter. 'What's the use of trying. I have no chance of succeeding', she says to herself.

Overweight

Being overweight is a great source of lack of confidence, because our society equates fat with inferior. All the images of the ideal woman that the media thrust before us are of slender women, the fat characters are usually reserved for the comedy roles. Our society, unlike many other cultures in the world, projects the image of the ideal woman as long-legged and slender, but in fact few women actually fulfil these expectations. The rest are encouraged to be over critical of themselves and consider their bodies as second best, which particularly affects girls in their super-sensitive teenage years. Food is associated with fat, eating with getting away from the popular slender silhouette, therefore eating equals failure.

Later women do come to realise that although physical attraction is important on first meetings, deep and lasting relationships are built on what the person is, not what they look like. However those who suffer from acute lack of confidence, find it easier to blame their loneliness on the fact they do not possess a perfect body. If a relationship turns sour, it is easier to blame it on the fact that she has put on weight rather than the idea that she is just not fun to be with any more.

The child who has been fat all her life will be used to being treated as second best. She never gets chosen for the school hockey team or for a part in the school play; she can't experiment with outrageous teenage fashions and doesn't get asked to dance by boys.

Being overweight leads to lack of confidence, and lack of confidence leads to eating problems, bingeing and extra weight, thus creating a vicious circle that traps the compulsive eater in a downward spiral. As confidence evaporates she becomes more and more aware of the ways in which she is failing to live up to the high standards she expects of herself. She begins to dread further failures which will further depress her and she lives with a constant fear of failure.

Most compulsive eaters have tried everything to control their eating. They have followed every diet ever devised, but have always failed to bring their weight and their eating under control. They reach the point where they no longer want to keep trying, rather not try at all than try and have to live with the feeling of failure. This attitude spreads into every corner of their lives and they restrict themselves so much they are merely existing and not living a full life.

A woman can become trapped in her home, she dreads even walking down the street because she feels people are looking at her. She dare not go shopping because she knows she may be tempted to steal food. She only feels safe inside her own home.

Not all compulsive eaters are women at home. Many are out in the world holding down top jobs, but their fears and anxieties are so great that they dare not express them through their work, so they cling to food for comfort. Failure makes her feel humiliated and ashamed and unable to face the world. A television station decided to put together a series of programmes about different social problems and although they were able to get drug addicts, alcoholics and even anorexics to talk about their problems, they could not find a compulsive eater prepared to come forward and be interviewed in public.

An accepted condition

Other compulsions have acceptable medical-sounding names that their victims can hide behind. The alcoholic and the drug addict have socially understandable reasons for their behaviour. But compulsive eating is little understood and not widely accepted as an illness. In the eyes of the world overeating problems are still equated with personality weaknesses, like greed and lack of will-power. The woman with an eating problem has to say to herself, 'I am a compulsive eater, I have an addiction to food, but in other ways I am no different from other people.' Even doctors often do not understand the deep-seated problems involved in compulsive eating, the humiliation and shame the woman feels and the way her obsession completely takes over her life.

If she goes to the doctor with a weight problem, he is likely to hand out a diet sheet and tell her all she has to do is stick to what is written on the paper and her problems will be over. If she fails, he loses patience with her and quickly runs out of sympathy. If she is not overweight, she is less likely to go to a doctor, but if she does she will probably find him even less sympathetic than if she weighed 18 stone. The compulsive eater, with her complex array of psychological hang-ups, can be utterly destroyed by other people's condemnation of her failure.

Fear of failure

Fear of failure leads to a fear of attempting projects, and so most compulsive eaters never reach anything like their full potential. Their lives become more and more limited as they restrict themselves to activities and surroundings they know they can cope with.

If you consider that you do draw back from attempting to achieve things through fear of failure, analyse the situation carefully and consider if you are, in fact, not more afraid of success. Failure is much easier than success. If you fail to lose weight or fail to fit into a social set, you can creep away and hide, feeling sorry for yourself. But if you succeed in your job, you will be under constant pressure to stay at the top and continue to do well; if you succeed in achieving your ideal weight you will feel under pressure to maintain it by constant diet. Talking endlessly about all the things you are planning to do is not the same as going out and doing them. So many people say that one day they are going to write a book, but in fact they rarely get further than the first page, because secretly they fear they might not be able to complete it or it might be no good. Fear of failing stifles ambition, so they do not attempt to write and gain pleasure from putting their ideas on paper because they fear the result may not be a best-seller.

Many people actually fear success. Success is the goal we all strive for, the prize we all dream of, but in fact how many let it all slip away just when it seems to be within their grasp. The pop group who struggle for years in pubs and clubs suddenly have a hit record, fame and fortune are there at last, but they throw it all away and are never heard of again. When face to face with success, it proved more than they could handle.

The poor man has nothing to lose, but if he becomes wealthy he will have to install a burglar alarm in his home and make sure all his possessions are locked and secure. The same principle applies to the personality, the more you succeed the more you have to lose and the greater the strain and effort required to hang on to it. Fear of success particularly applies to women. When the man is the breadwinner he is content, but if his wife starts to do well in her career, earn more than him and be more successful, it disturbs the fundamental balance of the sexes which still exists strongly in society despite modern emancipation.

This situation is seen time and again in show business where an up and coming actor marries an unknown, then overnight she becomes famous and wealthy and he is left in the shadows. Again it is a lot easier for a woman to be the Prime Minister's wife than for a man to be the husband of the Prime Minister.

Fear of success

Achieving success in one field also focuses attention on other areas which may not be so easy to cope with. If an eating problem is the way a woman expresses a deep-seated inability to cope with personal relationships, succeeding in controlling her eating will force her to direct her attention towards sorting out her relationship problems. She may find it easier to devote all her time to battling with her eating.

Success usually makes a person more prominent, and most compulsive eaters are those who hate to be in the limelight or singled out from the crowd. Many people contact the Maisner Centre for Eating Disorders in Brighton saying they are desperate for help with their problems. They enrol to begin treatment, but then disappear and are never heard of again. Many are afraid they will start the treatment and fail, in which case they will feel even more depressed, or alternatively they fear they will succeed, in which case a whole range of new and more difficult problems will emerge for them to have to face.

It takes time

Many compulsive eaters are very impatient in their search for a cure to their problems, they want instant success and cannot accept the fact that nobody is going to wave a magic wand and banish their problems overnight. Their compulsive eating did not arrive out of the blue one morning, it was a result of years, even a lifetime, of wrong eating habits, wrong attitudes and negative habits. Bringing about the fundamental changes of outlook and personality which are the only lasting way to control compulsive eating is a slow and painful business. They become easily discouraged and every setback is seen as proof of total failure. This exaggerates their fear of failure, boosts lack of confidence and puts an end to attempts at controlling their eating.

It is essential to understand that temporary setbacks do not mean permanent failure and confidence is necessary to see it in this light. There will be black days and it is then more than ever when it is vital to make a real effort. If you really want to get better, it is at these lowest times that it is essential to at least pick up the telephone and speak to someone. Be careful who you choose though, if you telephone your husband at the office when you know he is in the middle of an important business meeting, he will not be able to listen sympathetically, he will cut the conversation short and you will feel rejected and miserable. If you do not have a friend who understands your problem and can be relied upon to listen whenever you feel the need to telephone, find a professional counsellor and keep that telephone number handy for black days. If nobody is around, the Samaritans are always at the end of a telephone to listen.

Be honest with yourself

If you are not prepared to make this effort at black times, ask yourself honestly whether you really want to get over your eating problems. Of course you do, you reply immediately, doesn't every compulsive eater long to have her eating under control? Ask yourself again, how would you feel if you succeeded, what would you do with your life, could you live in a world that left you sufficient time to think about all the other demands that would be made upon you?

If you are feeling really low today, you blame it on yourself, on your inability to control your eating, your weakness, your personality failings. Look again at the reasons for your depression, could it be something else like premenstrual tension, the weather, the fact that you are overdrawn at the bank. Always put these things into their true perspective before leaping to the conclusion that it is you that is failing.

Boosting confidence

Shyness is itself a form of arrogance and bad manners and it makes other people uneasy; they feel uncomfortable in the presence of somebody who is so conscious of themselves all the time. But people feel equally uncomfortable with someone who appears faultless and reminds them of their own shortcomings. The best way to behave with others is to be yourself and not strive to appear anything better or worse.

If you are invited to a party and feel nervous and shy, boost your confidence before you go by spending time getting ready. Have a bath, wash your hair and put on makeup and clean, crisply ironed clothes. If you make an effort to make yourself look good, it shows you value yourself and this boosts your self-esteem.

The great thing to remember when struggling to make conversation if you are shy is that the vast majority of people are far more interested in themselves than in you. You may be overwhelmed with your own problems and see them as a barrier to conversation, but the other person is completely ignorant of all this and will be delighted to tell you all about their life. Ask polite questions, without appearing nosey, about their work, how are their children, or even what do they think of the weather, and they will talk for hours and think you wonderful company. Don't avoid parties just because you are shy, but if you honestly don't enjoy them, don't go. Have the confidence to admit to yourself that there are other more interesting things you would far rather be doing. Then go and do them.

Anybody can do anything if they really want to badly enough. Miracles do happen, and usually they are brought about through the determination of the person involved. When motor cycle ace Barry Sheen had a bad accident, they told him he would never race again, but he simply refused to believe them and within a few months was back on the track. Attitude is all important when it comes to success or failure; convince yourself that you can succeed and you want to succeed and refuse to consider failure for a single moment and you will get there in the end.

It is far easier to eat than to struggle to succeed at work, to create a warm loving atmosphere in the home, to always look slim and smart and smiling. Failure is the easy way out.

Nobody is perfect

Nobody can be perfect all the time, so while always striving for success it is also essential to be able to accept failure. Find an honest reason why you have slipped up and watch out that it does not happen again. Perhaps you are beginning to feel you really have your eating under control at last, than a traumatic situation crops up and you immediately turn to food for comfort. This does not mean all the good work you have done has disappeared, your binge was the direct result of one particular incident. It happened, it is now over, and you can return to your previous good efforts. It is the easy way out to make one binge the excuse for another and then another. On the road to controlling eating it is not necessarily the occasional binge that is important, but the way you react to it and the speed with which you can put it behind you and carry on with your life.

Asserting your determination to overcome the problem in such a situation is perhaps the most difficult task that a compulsive eater has to face. Self-assertion means being able to say no and mean it, both to yourself and to others.

Saying no

The root of being able to say no to things you do not want is a clear view of exactly what your needs are. For example, if you do not smoke and somebody offers you a cigarette it is easy to say, 'No, thank you, I don't smoke', and clearly express the message that you do not require a cigarette. If you have no eating problem and are not hungry and somebody offers you a piece of cake, it is simple and obvious to say no and mean it. The compulsive eater faced with the offer knows she longs to eat that slice of cake, and several more slices, so although she says no, inside she is saying yes. The person making the offer senses she really means to say yes and offers the cake again. Afraid of offending, the cake is accepted.

Answers like, 'I am on a diet' or 'I'll put on pounds if I eat all those calories' show the inner battle that is going on and are likely to bring well-meaning replies like, 'You can always go on a diet tomorrow.' A firm concise, 'No thank you, I don't eat cake', will put an end to the subject quickly and permanently. It only takes a moment to say, and you are unlikely to be pressed further.

Don't wait until the situation arises to start learning how to say no. Practise the scene over and over again when you are on your own. You are invited to visit your mother-in-law and know she will have made a lavish tea specially for you and will press you to eat more than you should. Before you go get your story straight and practise saying it. Something simple like, 'It was good of you to go to all this trouble, but I am not hungry', say it and mean it. She may be a little put out, but after you have visited her and firmly refused on several occasions she will get the message and no longer pressurise you into eating.

Sexual relationships

Making love is another area in which the compulsive eater's inability to say no causes her a lot of unnecessary anguish. She goes along with what her husband or boyfriend wants because she is constantly seeking his approval and cannot face the strain of disagreeing with him. Anything for a quiet life. If you want to say no, say no, but in such a way that will not leave him feeling angry or rejected. Vague excuses, like having a headache, are not satisfactory. You should tell him that you still love him, but just do not feel in the mood for it tonight. Sex is a partnership between two people, and you have just as much right to say yes or no as he does.

A single girl also comes under sexual pressure these days. She is afraid if she does not sleep with her boyfriend, he will go off and find someone else or tell his friends there is something wrong with her. Despite the media image there are many girls who prefer not to have sex until they have built up a deep, long-standing relationship with a man. But such is the reversal of Victorian ideas that often girls are embarrassed to admit this and go around giving the impression they are free and liberated. It takes self-confidence and self-assertion to say no and mean it. Your body is your own and it is up to you to choose whether you wish to share it with somebody else. If you do, it is their privilege; if you don't want to, don't.

Respect is still an important part of a sexual relationship. The old-fashioned warning that a man would not respect a woman

141

who lets him get too close before they were married no longer really applies. But today a man will not respect a woman who does what he wants just to hang on to him. He will sense her lack of enthusiasm and lose interest. If it is what she wants and she enjoys it as much as he does that is fine, but if she has the self-confidence to say no when she means it, he will respect her for her decision.

Asserting your rights is fundamental to building up the strength of character essential to overcoming your eating problems. If one person is doing all the giving and the other all the taking, it is not a true relationship.

Women in general tend to lack the ability to assert themselves and they allow resentment to build up, which in the compulsive eater leads to bingeing. If you are afraid to speak out and demand your rights look at the situation and consider the very worst thing that could possible happen if you were to assert yourself.

MARY is married to a selfish man and she gives in to him and lets him have his own way all the time, but she is seething inside with suppressed anger and resentment which poisons her life and leads her into food binges. She longs to invite her friends round one evening, but does not dare because she knows her husband will resent other women invading his home and make a scene. When she asserted her right to invite her friends into her home, he would sulk and go out to the pub and there was a nasty atmosphere for several days. She continued to stand up for her rights and refused to fuel his selfishness, and she had to face up to endless rows and sulks, but in time he came round to allowing her more freedom and they discovered they had more to talk about.

In such a case if he is allowed to continue to behave totally selfishly the worst that could happen might be a breakdown of the marriage, and in such a severe situation this might even prove beneficial to the woman and give her the opportunity to rebuild her own life. In reality the worst is never usually as bad as you fear, but you can only find this out by standing up for your rights, asserting yourself and facing the consequences.

142

What are your needs?

First make your needs clear to yourself, then to other people. Have the confidence to assert your demands on others and mean it, but don't assume they know your needs without you having to tell them.

BRIDGET was angry and resentful with her husband because he did not help her with the housework when she started a full-time job. Every time she felt herself left with the housework to do she would end up bingeing. Because she had always had everything in the house well-organised, it had never occurred to her husband that she might like some help, and he would have been happy to lend a hand if she had asked him. In this case her anger was misdirected because the real reason for her resentment was the fact that she had a full-time job, not that she had to do the housework. She was blaming him for her stupidity in taking on a job she did not want to do, and supporting this resentment by not telling him how she felt.

In this case Bridget talked to a third person about how she was feeling and this person tactfully suggested to her husband that he help her with the housework because she was tired. He was quite happy to help her and with the release of tension they were able to discuss her worries about her job and decide that she should go back to part-time work.

It is not easy to work out exactly what your wants or needs are, especially if you are depressed or in the grip of a compulsive habit. The compulsive eater often has difficulty in thinking about anything other than getting her eating under control. The way to do it is start with small things and take one day at a time, then gradually the things you truly need will become clearer to you. Don't begin by deciding to get rid of all your bad habits on the first day; you will fail and that will undermine your confidence still further.

Begin by deciding you will say no to something once a week. It can be anything that upsets you, not necessarily to do with food. Your neighbour asks to borrow the lawn mower just when you were planning to use it; instead of handing it over and waiting for them to bring it back, by which time it is too dark to do your lawn, assert yourself and say you are just about to use it, but they can borrow it when you have finished. Having politely told them this, get on with the job and don't feel guilty.

Exercise

When you are alone at home practise saying no in imaginary situations, or practise asking for something you really want. Work out the possible replies and how you would deal with them. Get into the mental habit of asserting your rights until you feel confident enough to say it out loud when the situation arises.

Sooner or later you have got to take a bit of a risk and face up to the possibility that your request might be refused and you will feel devastated with guilt and rejection. To begin with only ask for something small, something you can be fairly sure they will not say no to, and in this way your confidence will grow and you can begin to ask for bigger things.

Involve other people

Remember people like to be asked to do things for others, it makes them feel needed, so you are doing them a favour by asking them. Perhaps you feel your colleagues at work don't seem to include you in their social group, perhaps because you always refuse to go out to lunch with them. Why not ask one of them to come shopping with you one lunch time and help you choose a pair of shoes? She will probably be delighted to feel you respect her opinion.

The habit of never asserting yourself, never asking for things you want and never being able to say no are hard to break, and the longer you carry on living your life in this way, the deeper the habits become ingrained, and the harder they will be to break. Like every habit these things become comfortable and safe, like the baby who sucks its thumb. Do not be afraid of change, but again start making changes in small ways that will not threaten your sensitive ego.

Start by changing the furniture around, the armchair will not dislike you or reject you if you shift it from its usual placé next to the fire. Or buy a different daily paper which will give you a slightly changed look at the world.

If you suffer agonies from a sense of rejection, the answer is not to avoid all situations where you may be put in this position, but to learn to face up to them and cope with them. Success in this way boosts confidence and leads to a greater ability for self-assertion.

If the compulsive eater asks somebody to do something for her and they refuse she will immediately jump to the conclusion that the person does not like them, is rejecting them and fall back on a whole mass of self-centred reasons. In fact there may be some very good reason why they said no, perhaps your friend has a bad cold and does not want to pass it on, perhaps your boyfriend is under a lot of pressure at the office and dare not go out to meet you in his lunch hour in case he misses an urgent telephone call. Always look for the logical reason first before jumping to the conclusion they are turning you down because they dislike you, because you are depressed, or because they don't like the shape of your figure.

Skill with people

Social skills can be taught, just as manual skills can be taught, and there are classes that cover this sort of subject. (Ask at your local Adult Education Centre, at the Citizens' Advice Bureau or your nearest library. Also check the local newspapers for classes.) One exercise students are expected to attempt involves visiting the library once a week and making a point of saying hello to someone. The following week they return and say hello, isn't it a nice day today, and in this way they gradually build up a relationship quite safely and without any risk of rejection. Such social skills are practised within a group and then each person is expected to go and attempt to put what they have learnt into practice. If you are so shy you do not know your next door neighbour, knock on the door and ask to borrow a needle and thread, but do it sensibly, not when you have just noticed a car load of visitors arriving, or when they are likely to be sitting down to a meal.

A great boost to self-confidence is being able to talk with authority on a subject, so try and become an expert on something that interests you. It can be growing roses or breeding budgerigars, but don't bore everyone with your knowledge of nutrition and calorie counting. In this way you will have something to say and something to contribute to a conversation.

A dog is another confidence booster. A dog could not care less what size you are or how much cleverer your elder brother is, he returns your love in a simple honest way. Walking a dog in the park is a wonderful way of getting to know people, you don't have to make the effort of introductions, the dogs do it for you. Having a dog also means you are not alone in the house with all the dread and bingeing that can cause, and of course taking him out for walks is good exercise.

Expand your horizons

The compulsive eater will come up with an endless list of reasons for not doing all the things recommended to improve her self-confidence and overcome her eating problems. One excuse often given is that she has never done it before, which points to an obvious case of limited horizons where the best thing she can possibly do is break those restricting habits and plunge into something new.

'I'm too fat to go to aerobics' is another excuse: one girl joined a class and felt inferior because she was not as good as the other girls, so she secretly joined a couple of other classes at different centres and everyone at each class was amazed and full of admiration at the way she rapidly improved.

'I'm too shy to go to parties': is the gut-twisting cry of the girl who has probably lacked self-confidence all her life. Begin by going along to a friendly gathering with a girlfriend and gradually work your way into a social set. After you have been to a few get-together parties with the same group of people, they will become familiar and you will be confident enough to meet them

on your own and from there gradually expand your circle of friends. Joining a club or an evening class where everyone has a common interest is often an easier way of making friends than going to a discotheque or parties.

'People will think I'm different': many compulsive eaters say they are afraid to eat properly because others will notice them and think them different. Because other people tend to live on popular and junk foods, she feels she must do the same to conform. Just because everyone else in the household has cornflakes and toast and marmalade for breakfast does not mean that it is the ideal breakfast. As anyone following the eating plan should understand by now, protein is essential at the beginning of the day.

Don't be afraid to eat the sort of meals you know you should be eating. Prepare them quietly without making a fuss or drawing attention to what you are doing and probably others will not even notice you are eating something different. If they do remark, have the confidence to stand up for the fact that you are the one who has got it right as far as diet is concerned.

'People will look at me': fear that people will look at you, will talk about your figure or guess at your secret problems keep many compulsive eaters shut away from social gatherings. The straight facts about that is that the majority of people are far too busy looking at themselves and worrying about what you are thinking about them to give much thought to you and your problems. In fact, however huge your own problems may seem to you, you never have to go far to find someone with troubles a whole lot worse, and that is a great help in getting your own life into proportion.

It is easy to become so obsessed with yourself and your own failures that you completely disregard your successes. You only remember how disgustingly you behaved by eating too much on holiday and forget the lovely scenery and sunshine enjoyed and the nice people you met. You can only think about the day you binged and forget the week of good healthy eating that you kept to so well. This is just lack of confidence in yourself and your ability to succeed in controlling your eating.

Most people with eating problems find it difficult to eat in front of others. If this is your problem discover why exactly it worries you. If you are afraid others will think you are greedy start by tackling the problem a stage at a time, begin by sharing half an orange or half an apple with someone. Join up with another compulsive eater and have a snack together. Remember eating is a perfectly natural function. Everyone does it. People are much more likely to notice you if you are the only one not eating.

Test your self-confidence

Now test your own self-confidence and ability to assert yourself by looking at the way you would handle the following situations. How would fear of failure or fear of success affect the way you cope?

1.   After dinner there is a programme you particularly want to watch on television, but you know 'Top of the Pops' is on the other channel. Do you:

(a)   Tell your teenage children it is their turn to do the washing up for a change, and point out that they watch whatever they want every evening, now it is your turn to watch what you want.
(b)   Make some grumbling comment about awful pop music and disappear into the kitchen in a huff.
(c)   Keep smiling as you tackle the washing up single-handed and have an extra something to eat to console yourself.

Situation (a) is familiar to all parents. Television rules in most homes and teenagers can be very difficult to stand up to, especially when their favourite pop group is involved. Being firm about how much television they watch and how big a contribution they make to household chores should begin when they are small; trying to impose it at 14 is asking for rebellion and family discord.

In situation (b) you are not making your needs clear to the family. They have not been told that you want to watch a programme on the other side and so are not given the chance of allowing you to see it. You might be afraid that if it comes to an argument over which channel you watch, you might lose. On the other hand you might win and they all go off to do something else leaving you alone with the television set and a programme that wasn't really worth watching after all. In this case your success would prove rather sour.

Situation (c) is the true compulsive eater who would not dare stand up for her rights and does not even try, she just sneaks off and has a binge.

2.   Your boyfriend enjoys going to the pictures but you are not very keen on all those war and spy films. Do you:

(a)   Suggest you see something a little more romantic occasionally or that you go to a theatre or a dance sometimes instead of the cinema each week.
(b)   Say you don't want to go to the cinema with him each week, you have joined a pottery class and he can either meet you afterwards or find another girl to go with.
(c)   Keep trailing along to those boring films each week and sit in the dark nibbling all the chocolates and popcorn.

Give and take are the most important things in a successful relationship. In situation (a) you are prepared to indulge his passion for war films to a certain extent, but stand up for your rights to the sort of entertainment you enjoy from time to time.

(b) is rather drastic, unless you are not keen on him anyway and looking for an excuse to break off the relationship. Perhaps he is not really that keen on the cinema either, but can't think of anything else to do when you go out together. Try to communicate.

In situation (c) you lack the confidence to tell him what you feel in case he doesn't want to see you anymore and you are left without a boyfriend. Food is the only comforter for this poor girl; if she marries him she will be a doormat all her life.

3.   You hear there is another girl living near you who also suffers from the compulsive eating habit. Do you:

149

(a)   Telephone and ask if she would like you to go round and visit her.

(b)   Write her a letter explaining the situation and suggest you might get together or become pen friends to help each other with your mutual problem.

(c)   Write that letter, but never post it.

Situation (a) shows you understand all the pitfalls of compulsive eating. You know that the two of you together can help each other through black times, but you also realise she may be too shy to come and visit you in a strange house so you are prepared to make the effort to go to her.

In situation (b) you are too shy to risk direct contact, over the telephone she might say something that would make you feel rejected, but a letter is an easier form of introduction.

Situation (c) is a typical display of lack of confidence. You know getting together with another compulsive eater would help you and you have good intentions of doing something about it. But when it comes to the point, your fear of not being able to get on with her, or your fear that your joint efforts might actually prove successful, prevent you posting the letter.

Confidence is something that grows slowly, don't expect to wake up one morning and find yourself transformed from a shy little Cinderella to a radiantly confident princess – it just doesn't happen like that, except in fairy tales. But once you begin to break out of your shell and begin developing self-confidence, it will snowball and after a while you will be able to look back with satisfaction on the progress you have made. Vast new horizons open up for the person who has the confidence to explore their world.

CHAPTER FIFTEEN

Getting Out of the Rut

The only real death is the death we die every day
by not living.

Zorba
Nikos Kazantzakis

Boredom is a downward spiral. The more bored you are the less
able you are to do anything about it. Being bored is an
exhausting occupation. There is nothing more tiring than doing
nothing.

Are you bored?

Boredom is not the same thing as having nothing to do. It can be
very pleasant to sit and do nothing for hours, and you don't feel
the slightest bit bored if you feel content to sit in the sun or
amble along beside the sea or walk through the snow. On the
other hand you can be working away all day and be bored to
tears even though you don't stop and rest for a moment. If you
are not enjoying what you do or getting any fulfilment out of it
it becomes boring.

Imagine ironing fourteen shirts. Unless you really get
pleasure from smoothing out wrinkles and watching the pile of
ironing grow, it is just a boring chore. You labour away because
it has to be done, putting in the minimum of effort and
enthusiasm and getting nothing back for your efforts.

Get out of the rut

There are always certain boring jobs in life that have to be done, but these can be cut down to a minimum by careful planning. Some people get away with never doing any ironing by persuading their husbands into drip-dry shirts, smoothing sheets while they are still damp, and all sorts of ingenious tricks.

So many people are bored at work. They clock on every day just to get their pay packet at the end of the week, and during working hours they put the minimum effort and interest into their job and get the minimum satisfaction out of it. Another person can be quite happy and fulfilled doing a similar job for years. It is very much an attitude of mind.

Even if you have a monotonous, menial job at the bottom of the ladder, by showing enthusiasm and initiative the opportunity for promotion will quite often come along. Many people who are now on the top rung started right at the bottom, on the shop floor or in the filing room, and worked their way up by making the best of whatever job they were given.

Don't just sit there thinking about food, about your figure, and about how quickly it will be time to go home. Take an interest in how the company works and try to work out ways of doing your job more efficiently.

Even if you have a boring job, there is no need to have a boring life outside the office. Your private life is completely in your own hands. Are you doing anything creative? Have you any hobbies (apart from eating)? Are you making any effort to go out and meet people? No wonder you are bored.

Excuses, excuses

'It's all very well for working girls to go out every night. I have got small children so I have to stay at home all the time': what a familiar cry. Half the housewives in the country sit back and grumble about their family being a tie to their creativity, while the other half are out and about doing something about it. Children are only a tie if you choose to make them one. There are plenty of interesting things you and your children can do together, even making the beds can be anything but boring if your two-year old is allowed to 'help'.

Every town has mother and toddler groups. If there is not one near you, why not start one by putting a card in the newsagent's window asking other mums to get in touch. When the children are at school, organise your day so that you have time for the things you want to do during school hours, and in the holidays arrange regular outings or special things to do at home to prevent the whole family from becoming bored.

Find another mum with children of a similar age to your own and arrange to look after each other's children occasionally, or on a regular basis, so you both have the chance of a day out on your own now and again or even get a part-time job.

'Going out and doing things costs money and I haven't got any': the first answer to that, of course, is how much are you spending on binge foods, or are you committing too much of your income to the wrong things? There are plenty of hobbies that don't cost anything or very little, from jogging to embroidery. Keeping a pet, even fish, is a fairly low-cost occupation for the amount of enjoyment and companionship you get in return. A small dog eats little, but still needs walks in the park.

There are even spare-time occupations that can earn you money. Think of the constant stream of advertising literature and free newspapers that come through your letterbox. Someone has to deliver them, or perhaps there are people who would pay you to walk their dogs each day. Both these occupations involve cash and exercise.

If you had a skill at one time, try putting it to use, for example hairdressers doing people's hair at home, a nurse sitting with an elderly person while the family go shopping. Your local branch of the WRVS or Citizens' Advice Bureau will put you in touch with opportunities for voluntary work (look for their address in the telephone directory). Charities often need people to collect jumble, sell flags and generally help with money-raising schemes. There is nothing better than doing something for somebody else to make you forget your own problems as well as banish your boredom. But whatever you do or become involved in, take an interest and give something of yourself to it.

'It all sounds a good idea, but I just haven't got the energy': as we have already said, there is nothing more tiring than doing nothing. Join an exercise class and shake up that weary body and get your system moving, you will find you have got energy you never

knew you possessed. People who are engrossed in what they are doing never feel tired, those who are busy can keep going for hours.

A curious toddler is never bored. He just goes on and on exploring and discovering until weariness catches up with him and he falls asleep. Watch a dog in the park. He keeps following his nose from one new smell to the next and runs for miles without getting tired, but if you don't take him out for a walk he will sleep in front of the fire all day. Interest and an enquiring mind don't recognise tiredness.

Weariness is usually a state of mind rather than body unless you can honestly say that you have been exerting yourself all day. The greatest effort of all is required to heave yourself out of the rut of boredom and inactivity. After that the energy is always there for what you have an interest in.

Give and take

The more effort you put into something the more you get out of it. That applies to housework, typing letters and also to tackling your eating problems. Setting about sorting out your life and your eating must be a total commitment; half-hearted attempts will not succeed because you will soon become bored with it all.

Are you filling in the charts each day with details of your eating? Or has that already got to be a bit of a chore, you can't be bothered to do it every day? Before long you will give up completely.

If you do not commit yourself to follow every exercise given in this book and commit yourself to giving this method of overcoming your problems a fair and energetic trial, you cannot expect to succeed, you will just get bored with all of it and give up, then say the method doesn't work. Just like you did with your last diet ... and the one before that.

Everything's so boring

Are you deluding yourself that somebody else is responsible for your boredom? We all have control over our own lives and our own thoughts and emotions. If you are bored, it is your fault and nobody else's.

Is your husband or partner a boring person? How much interest do you take in him. How much effort do you put into understanding his football talk or his job? If all you can think about is calories and your weight you must be even more boring than he is.

If you feel you have no friends, or there is nobody that you like enough to bother with, that is because you are not putting yourself forward as a friendly person who attracts the friendship of others. You are too wrapped up in yourself to give anything away and others find you too boring to bother with.

Do you feel bored with that diet of crispbread, cottage cheese and lettuce? No wonder you are obsessed with the idea of food. Just because food has not got a lot of calories it does not have to be dull. There are endless possibilities for exciting salads and really tasty vegetable dishes. Start experimenting with herbs and spices, unusual combinations of tastes and textures. Put imagination into your meals and they will no longer be boring to prepare or eat.

Are you bored with the way you look? That same dreary frowning face in the mirror is enough to make anyone feel depressed. Give yourself a new image, a drastic new hairstyle, contact lenses. Smile. It is amazing how a smile can alter the way you look. If you have a bright smiling face people don't even notice the size of your hips.

If you are just bored by your whole lifestyle, change it. Start by putting on some lively music to change the mood, redecorate your living room, start learning French conversation from records while you peel the potatoes. In other words wake up your imagination and change the negative boredom into positive achievement.

CHAPTER SIXTEEN

Loneliness

All the lonely people,
Where do they all come from?
All the lonely people,
Where do they all belong?
'Eleanor Rigby'
Lennon and McCartney

How lonely you are depends very much on your attitude to the rest of the world. Loneliness is very much a state of mind and is largely self-imposed, often without the lonely person realising it. They blame the rest of the world for neglecting them instead of going out to make contact with others. Do you often choose to be alone so that you can binge?

Fear of making a fool of yourself, fear of rejection by others, especially after the break-up of a relationship, are common reasons for loneliness, and in such cases the only 'friend' to turn to is food. Food comforts and consoles, at the same time it does not make any demands of commitment and personal relationship so it provides an easy prop to lean on when making your way in society seems just too daunting.

Are you lonely?

Being lonely is not the same thing as being alone. It can be very pleasant to have time to yourself, in fact everyone needs some time each day to be on their own. Even in childhood parents should encourage their children to learn to amuse themselves as well as to socialise with other children and adults. But you can always have too much of a good thing, and there are estimated to be very few true 'loners' in the world. Most people who say

156

they prefer to be on their own all the time are, in fact, saying they cannot, or will not, get on with their fellow human beings.

Being alone only becomes loneliness when the person feels they are missing the companionship of others and are in some way a social failure. If you were shipwrecked alone on a desert island, you might say it is no fault of your own you are lonely, but living in a city or even a village you are surrounded by other people. All you lack is the ability to relate to them.

Exercise
Ask yourself these questions and think carefully about the answers you give.

1 Do you consider you are lonely?
2 Do you consider yourself in tune with the people around you?
3 Do you have interests and activities in common with people you know?
4 Is there anyone you feel really close to, or do all your relationships seem rather superficial?
5 Do you feel there are other people you can turn to or do you think that nobody really understands you?
6 What do you feel you have to offer to other people, do you ever attempt to offer it?

Loneliness can come at any age

Anybody can be lonely, from a baby to a pensioner. Among younger people times of greatest loneliness often coincide with times when bingeing is most likely, for example students and young mothers.

Girls studying for school examinations or at college or university are going through a period of great insecurity and change and during their teens often either give in to loneliness or go to exaggerated lengths to avoid it. Leaving home and going to college often means being on their own in unfamiliar surroundings for the first time, and it is then that many students turn to food for comfort.

157

So many young people end up going to parties they don't enjoy or trailing around with groups of people they don't really like, doing things they don't really want to do just so that they do not feel left out. But the one with an eating problem has an extra difficulty to face up to. Perhaps her friends all decide to buy fish and chips on the way home from the cinema, either she decides not to go to the cinema because she knows it will mean fish and chips on the way home, or she goes along with the gang and eats more calories than she intended. If she stays at home alone feeling lonely and resentful she is likely to binge and end up eating far more calories than are to be found in a portion of fish and chips. However, if she does not want to see the film, does not like the rest of the gang or has a lot of work that needs doing urgently, she should refuse to go and not feel socially deprived. Food should never be a reason for inflicting loneliness upon yourself.

The new mother who has been out at work and recently given up her job so often falls into the loneliness trap. All her former friends are busy working during the day, and somehow she no longer has much in common with them any more. Although she never seems to have a minute to herself with her baby making constant demands on her attention, she feels bored and lonely. Because she has always been out at work she does not know many of her neighbours, and her husband is wrapped up in his work, concerned about the responsibility of supporting his new family, and has little time to be a companion to her.

When the children get older they soon begin to develop their own interests; they go to school, make their own friends, enjoy their own hobbies, and no longer need the mother who has built her world totally around them. At this stage it is more important than ever to be the one who makes the first step outwards, there are so many lonely young mothers around all waiting for someone else to be the first to offer the hand of friendship. Getting out of the house is essential, because the more you shut yourself away with food the easier it will be to binge.

If you know your worst time of the day for bingeing is 11 am or 5 pm get into the habit of putting the baby in his pushchair and going for a walk at that time. If your problem is in the evening when you are alone or your husband is too tired to be sociable, make a commitment to join an evening class or club that will get you out of the house. Babies always survive if their mothers go away and leave them for an hour or two once a week. Never feel guilty about leaving your children with a baby sitter now and again, it will do them good to get used to having someone different around. The best thing you can do for your children is to be happy and contented in yourself, they will appreciate you much more for this than if you are always there but are miserable and bingeing.

In later years the break-up of a marriage or the death of a parent or partner can leave you feeling completely alone. The grief of such a loss also robs you of the strength and vitality to begin life over again and it is very easy to slip into the comfortable habit of eating instead. The media don't help, and watching too much television can often exaggerate the situation. Television is largely about relationships, even the advertisements rarely show less than two people, so for those who feel they are alone, this adds to their sense of isolation.

The only answer is to go out and do things and meet people. Even if you feel you can't face people and you are not enjoying what you are doing, stick at it and in time you will find new friends and new interests. If you shut yourself away, you are closing yourself off from the *possibility* of social contact; by being among people the opportunity of building a new social life is always nearby.

Take the risk

There is always an element of risk in taking on anything new, whether it is a boyfriend, a mortgage or a trip on a space rocket. There is always the possibility that the boyfriend will break your heart or the spaceship will crash, but if you never try you never find out and you miss out on the possibility of a wonderful experience.

Nobody wants to be rejected or make a fool of themselves in public, but it happens to everyone at some time or another.

Being afraid of these things does not in fact make them any less likely to happen, in fact fear is likely to attract that very disaster you try so hard to avoid. You have to learn to go out and face these things and discover that they don't really matter. So what, some people don't want to know you, that's their loss, they are denying themselves the pleasure of your company probably because they have got as many problems with socialising as you have.

Why haven't you got any friends?

Do you really feel you haven't got a friend in the world, while your sister is so popular she is always surrounded by a crowd? Ask yourself why you are on your own; is it because you are unable to think about anything but food and so have nothing to offer a friend? Friendship is very much a two-way thing. How much are you giving to others, or do you have such an uncontrollable temper that people avoid you? Talking too much can put people off just as much as not saying a word. Do you really listen to what others are saying to you, or are you too wrapped up in your own problems?

What to do about it

Nature abhors a vacuum, so if loneliness is creating a void in your life you are driven to fill it with food. You must learn to fill that empty space with something else, not just activity but a fulfilling and pleasing occupation and happy contented thoughts. You can't invite people round to dinner every night, or spend your whole life in a crowd, even if you did you might still be lonely. The way to beat loneliness is to develop a different attitude about yourself and other people and balance your life with periods of companionship and times when you are happy to be on your own.

Commitment is a word that horrifies most compulsive eaters, but is essential if you want to become part of a social group. Others soon get tired of the person who only turns up when it suits her without considering whether others will be inconvenienced by her absence. They are not going to keep inviting you round when you always make excuses not to go (you don't give them the real reason which is you can't commit yourself to a date in case you are bingeing on that day).

So pay for a course of aerobics in advance, don't just pay if and when you bother to turn up. Join a class and accept that if you are shy you will probably stand in the corner and not speak to anyone on the first evening, but you all have an interest in common and after a few weeks even the most shy person begins to get to know the rest of the class. If you receive an invitation accept it without question, make a date and BE THERE.

Christmas, Easter, holidays and weekends can be very alarming for the lonely person, if they feel they are the only person in the world not having a good companionable time the result is sure to be the binge. Make plans well in advance for these times, but don't expect your friends to be around on Christmas Day if they have to visit their families. Save up to go to a hotel or even abroad for Christmas, otherwise invite a few elderly people who live alone to share your Christmas dinner, or even children from a children's home if you prefer younger company.

It is not necessary to have vast amounts of friends to avoid being lonely. One or two good friends and a circle of acquaintances is as much as most people need if they have also found the secret of enjoying their own company now and again without feeling lonely. Never rely solely on one person for all your social needs, whether it is a friend, a husband or a child you are very vulnerable if all your emotional eggs are in one basket, and you are putting an intolerable burden on that person. Most people can find one person who is 'special', but they also need other friends.

Exercise
Having friends means being a friend to other people, so set yourself the target of speaking to somebody new every day and saying something nice to them. For example, compliment the girl on the supermarket checkout on the colour of her nail varnish, admire somebody's dog or their baby. Not only will you

be extending your ability to be friendly, you will possibly be making their day.

How others dealt with loneliness

The worst time for bingeing is usually when you are alone in the house, and Marilyn and Katherine both had this problem, one managed to come to terms with her loneliness that led to bingeing, the other did not.

MARILYN is happily married and she only binges on Tuesdays and Thursdays when her husband works late and she is alone in the house in the evenings. She will not go out on her own, she says she does not think she should be out enjoying herself while her husband is working. Marilyn has no other friends, her husband is the centre of her life and she gives him all her attention, so when he is not there she feels lost and binges. When asked, her husband said he would much rather she went out and enjoyed herself on Tuesday and Thursday evenings than he come home to find her vomiting and miserable. But Marilyn refuses to change her life because she feels a need to make her husband feel guilty. She is bingeing to try and punish him for leaving her alone.

KATHERINE Her bingeing nights were also a Tuesday and a Thursday when her husband was late home and she was alone in the house. But she now has a friend who, like Katherine, has a young baby and they take it in turns to visit each other on those evenings, so now Katherine no longer binges on those nights.

CHAPTER SEVENTEEN

The Woman's Role

Woman is the confusion of man.
Chaucer

During the twentieth century the role of women in society has altered radically and with such speed that many women have been left breathless in the race or have fallen by the wayside in the mad chase for equality. In trying to discover a new identity as people, they have often neglected their identity as women and feel lost, muddled and confused.

The whole attitude of society has shifted away from the traditional contrast of masculine and feminine towards a middle ground which has a general leaning towards the male. In Victorian times in particular all women were lumped together into the weak, emotional mould and all men into the strong aggressive mould, whether it suited their natures or not. Today there is a more enlightened view that permits women to get ahead in a competitive world and men to wear bright clothes, but this has also removed much of the stability of society.

In a recent survey people were asked to compile their idea of the 'normal' person from lists of qualities considered relevant to the male and to the female branches of society. Male qualities were such things as independence, objectivity, competitiveness, self-confidence, while female qualities were such things as illogical, not skilled in business, not adventurous, cries easily, never acts as leader. Most people included a high percentage of the male qualities in their ideal person.

If our society is shifting towards the male orientated what is left for the woman with a deep natural femininity? Compulsive eating is one way in which this inability to accept present day standards is expressed; many of those 'female' qualities are found strongly expressed in women with eating problems. They feel uncomfortable about asserting themselves and being independent and their feelings are easily hurt.

The traditional role

The role of woman as homemaker has been seriously undermined, leaving many who were content, satisfied and secure in such a way of life feeling lost and cheated. No longer is the housewife the pillar of society, the cornerstone of family life, in fact there is almost a sense of shame today in being 'just a housewife'. It is the basic natural instinct of the female to build a home and nurture her offspring and yet only the human species seems to want to deny this. Much stability in society and the family has been lost because the traditional way of life has been weakened.

The modern role

Those women who really benefit from the change in society are probably in the minority. Go-getting women, the high achievers who were once stifled by social conventions, now have the freedom they craved and are putting it to good use. They will also be unlikely to have eating problems if they have got their lives so well under control. Despite all the new legislation, women know that it is still very much a male-orientated world, to succeed a woman has to be twice as good and work twice as hard as her male equivalent. This puts tremendous pressure on those who want to do well in a career and the stress often drives them towards compulsive eating. Girls are educated to expect more out of life than their grandmothers and great-grandmothers, but if these expectations are not fulfilled they can feel let down and resentful. Feelings of inadequacy and underachievement foster a tendency to turn to food. It is not the woman who feels fulfilled in her career or content as a wife and mother who has the eating problem, but the one who feels somewhere along the line she is missing out on the wealth of opportunities other women seem to be enjoying.

MARILYN married two years ago and has a nice home and a secure and loving relationship with her husband. Now she feels she is expected to start a family, but she has eating problems which nobody knows about and feels she is not fit either physically or emotionally for the responsibilities of parenthood. 'My parents believed girls did not need careers and that I would work as a secretary, then marry and live happily ever after,' she said. 'I feel hemmed in though because I have achieved none of the things I wanted before I planned to settle down and have children.'

The middle path

Most women end up trying to walk a middle path between home and career, but it takes a lot of luck and wisdom to achieve this satisfactorily. It is too easy to attempt to take on too much and never succeed in anything. If a woman wants a home, children and a career she needs to be something of a juggler to keep everything spinning around nicely in a well-balanced way or she may end up with it all in ruins. A girl may plan a career, then fall in love and abandon everything to fit in with her man's life-style and bring up his children. Sooner or later her new life fails to satisfy her and she begins to regret the opportunities she threw away. Resentment begins to appear and if not expressed openly this can be a major reason for turning to the comfort of food.

KATE married and had a baby and she was happy for a year as a wife and mother. Then she began to long for the chance to go out on her own and have a bit of freedom because basically she felt bored with being at home with a small child all day and this was leading to eating problems. She tended to blame her husband for all her problems and admitted, 'I sometimes think I would like to be free of men entirely.'

Alternatively there is the woman who denies her natural instincts towards motherhood and builds a career, then when she approaches the menopause she realises she has lost out on things that many other women have and she in turn feels cheated and begins to harbour resentment.

Wife and mother

A lot of women just do not possess a strong maternal instinct and feel guilty because it is lacking. They let themselves be swept along into marriage and motherhood because they lack the self-assertion to admit they do not have any strong inclinations for it. An intelligent woman may feel totally unfulfilled by motherhood, even though she loves her children. If she does not have enough to occupy her mind with a modern home and one or two children she will become bored, frustrated and resentful, all key causes of eating problems.

This situation can also arise where a career woman has come under pressure to have children and has given in against her wishes, leaving her feeling resentful. If a single girl finds she is making too many excuses for not marrying and having children, she should ask herself if she is honestly standing up for the kind of life she wants for herself or whether she is just putting off a close relationship because it frightens her. Many single girls live at home long after they are old enough to fend for themselves, and their basic fear and insecurity is reflected in eating problems.

DEIRDRE was 26 and thought it was really time she left home and went to live on her own, but her parents liked having her at home, and she felt secure and well loved by everyone. She had never formed a lasting relationship with a man, because she said the only man she had ever loved was her father and she did not want to get married until she met someone like him. On the surface she appeared content, but her eating problems reflected the fact that she was not really happy with her life and felt unfulfilled.

Avoiding relationships

If a woman does not want a relationship with a man for deep-seated reasons of her own, eating can be a way of keeping men out of her life. If she is totally taken up with food, there will be no time to think of relationships. She will say that the right man will come along when she has got over her eating problems, or when she has reached her ideal weight, but at the same time she makes sure that day never comes.

> SUE was 32 years old and although she had had boyfriends she had never considered getting married. 'I don't ever want children,' she said. 'I don't feel I can really look after myself yet. I can't cope with responsibility and I can't handle my eating, so I certainly could not cope with children.'

On the other hand Sue may be unable to cope with the fact that she cannot seem to make or keep deep and lasting relationships with men. She blames it on her eating, saying that is the reason why she has not met the right man. She tells herself she will meet him when she slims down to a certain weight, so she diets and loses weight and still he does not come along, so she continues to diet and get thinner and thinner until she becomes really ill, but still the ideal man fails to appear.

Size and weight have nothing at all to do with meeting an ideal partner, unless the person chooses to make it an obstacle to forming relationships. Lots of fat people are happily married, and so are lots of slim people, weight is just a convenient excuse for deeper reasons.

While some compulsive eaters do not have relationships with men because there is no room in their lives for anything but their food obsessions, others have many relationships, sometimes to the extent of promiscuity, but none of them ever advance beyond the physical and the temporary. These are the women who are unable to commit even a corner of themselves to another person. As soon as there is any sign of an emotional attachment they withdraw.

The stress of relationships

Intense relationships often involve stress, and the compulsive eater knows she is unable to control her eating when under stress. Modern marriage makes great demands on the wife, not only is she the partner who runs the domestic household but she is expected to be a companion, mistress and counsellor as well. Many women are just not suited to these kinds of demands and it is not surprising that so many compulsive eaters suffer from relationship and marriage problems.

PAMELA was married to a man she adored, but right from the start she realised she would always have to share his affections with his mother. She grew very resentful of her mother-in-law and dreaded their weekly visits for Sunday lunch. She got very upset during these visits, although she never let her feelings show in front of her mother-in-law. Instead she would binge every Saturday night when she thought of the following day, and sometimes she binged so much she was unable to go with her husband on a Sunday.

The enforced intimacy of marriage exaggerates the problems of the secretive compulsive eater. If she is unable to share with her husband her guilty secret obsession, which is the most important thing in her life, how can she hope to achieve a deep and lasting relationship.

SARAH had been a compulsive eater since she was a teenager, although few people realised she had this problem. When she got engaged to John she was very happy and convinced that once she was married she would be starting a new life, her eating problems would disappear and they would 'live happily ever after'. She did not tell John about her eating problems, and he had never even heard of bulimia nervosa so it came as a shock to him to find out what was going on after they were married. For the first few weeks Sarah had managed to keep her eating fairly under control, but once the routine of marriage began to settle in, she found she was bingeing and vomiting more violently than ever.

'John finds my eating problem very frightening and does not understand it,' she said. 'He often reacts by becoming very angry and suspicious, he watches me all the time and treats me like a criminal. I wish I hadn't told him.'

A similar situation faces the single girl when a man telephones to make a date. She turns him down with some kind of excuse because she is quite unable to tell him the truth which is that she might be bingeing on that day, or she might be feeling fat and unable to go out.

In a marriage where the wife is a compulsive eater, the husband is probably aware that something is wrong but will prefer to push the problem aside. Where a woman has come for counselling and had to tell her husband about her eating, the result is nearly always beneficial. There is a sense of relief that the problem has come out into the open and the husband can see a concrete reason for his wife's behaviour. Whether the marriage ultimately survives or not depends on how they face the future together. If a rift does occur, it is not the revelation of something the husband probably knew already that causes it.

Sexual problems

Very few marriages or long-term relationships between men and women do not have sex problems at some time, and if the wife is a compulsive eater this is usually inevitable. If she feels fat, bloated and ugly, she will not appreciate his advances, and if she has been bingeing she will not want sex.

He feels she is rejecting him, and in time will begin to lose interest in her, so in turn she begins to feel rejected, even angry and aggressive, and the whole relationship enters a downward spiral. Many women want and enjoy sex for its own sake. However, occasionally, some women provide sex as a means of having the attention of their chosen man focused on them, but he will find it difficult to show her the attention and interest she desires if she has a constant air of depression around her. Who wants to make love to a woman who has forgotten how to laugh, to smile and to enjoy herself?

169

Women long for romance, hence the insatiable market for romantic fiction, but most men in real life are not a bit dashing and adventurous. If a man is not the romantic type nothing is going to change him, it is no good expecting him to act differently when you are married, when you have a baby, when you are slim.

ANN went to live with her father at the age of 9 after her parents separated, and because they lived in one small room she had to share a bed with her father. As an adult she discovered she could not face sex; she said she 'hates' it and realises it is because her father 'did things' to her when she was younger. Two years ago she married a man she adores, and because she loves him she tolerates sex, but at the same time she resents it, so she eats and eats. She says that eating makes her feel better, then she makes herself sick to 'punish' her husband. Ann was advised to see a marriage guidance counsellor to help her sort out her feelings before irreparable damage was done to the marriage.

Family finances

Compulsive eating can become a very expensive habit, and the financial complications that result can be a great cause of problems within a marriage. If the wife does not tell her husband she has an eating problem, how can she explain where the money is going, and in severe cases bulimics may spend up to £100 a day on food. After sex, money is probably the biggest cause of marriage breakdowns, and where the wife is a compulsive eater this is even more true.

Living in isolation

The disappearance of traditional family life affects women greatly. They feel guilty about not cooking a roast dinner on Sunday, even though the family have other things they want to do and are pleased not to be committed to eating it. For a woman food is the centre of family life, it is the time when her husband and children meet together round the table. Preparing a meal is probably the most creative thing she does for them and through food she can show her love and all her instincts for caring and nurturing. Where meals are no longer a family affair, she can feel cheated and resentful, but today it is common for the children to snatch a bite before rushing off to other activities and the husband to have his meal on a tray in front of the television.

The breakdown of family life has led to much more isolation. Families move away from their roots and there are no longer parents, grandparents and aunts close by. Many women find themselves completely alone in a hostile environment, separated from all the things that comforted them in their childhood. All except food that is. Often the wife who is a compulsive eater dreads being left alone in the house, even though at the same time she does not want to go out. She can become very clinging towards her husband and demand he stay at home with her.

CAROL spends the whole day looking after one 4 year old child, she says she is too tired to do anything else. She feels everything she does must be for her child and her husband and she should not do anything for herself. She managed to sort out with her husband that she would go out once a week while he stayed at home to babysit, so she joined an evening class and for a time did well. But after a while she became convinced that if she could go out once a week her husband and child did not really need her, her role as a wife and mother felt threatened and in this case going out was not the answer. She was advised to start doing things for herself within her home, like taking half an hour to read a magazine or have a leisurely bath. She was also told that by taking her child along to a playgroup she would be doing something for him by giving him independence and contact with other children, while at the same time she would be getting away from her house without feeling guilty.

Having children

Pregnancy is often a time when a woman puts on weight and after the child is born she is faced with a figure that is very different from the one she had a year ago. A crash diet to get rid of the extra weight, combined with the general stress of caring for a new baby, makes this a common time for eating problems to begin. Looking after a small child can be very boring, especially for an intelligent woman who is used to a demanding career, and it is very easy to turn to food during those long hours alone in the house. Little habits creep in, like eating up the children's leftovers and buying crisps, sweets and ice cream 'for the children' and eating them herself. Guilt begins to appear and resentment because she feels tied to the house.

Later there are the stormy confrontations of teenage years which put a lot of stress on any parent. Inability to cope with the trauma and battles means turning to food more and more. As they grow up a mother can feel let down because her children don't seem to need her any more or appreciate all she has done and sacrificed for them. Finally they leave home and she is left with an empty house and little to do to keep herself busy, but they frequently come home or telephone every time they have a problem. These are all the kinds of emotional situations that lead to a mother turning to food if she has an eating problem.

Children's eating problems

If a mother has a weight problem she is likely to go to great lengths to make sure her children do not suffer in the same way, to the extent of sowing the seeds of compulsive eating in them. Being continually obsessed with what your children can and can't eat as a reflection of your own eating obsessions can make them over-aware of their own eating habits.

JOANNA's mother was overweight as a teenager. She had wanted to lose weight, but her mother would not allow her to diet, so she was thoroughly miserable throughout her teenage years. So when Joanna showed signs of putting on weight as a child, she was forced to lose it. Although her mother's intention was to spare Joanna the miseries of being a fat teenager, in fact she drove her to steal food and go on secret binges until she realised the emotional effect this was having on her daughter. She then stopped punishing her for putting on weight and encouraged her to eat properly.

Overweight children are teased at school and become very emotionally upset, this sensitivity is made worse if too much emphasis is put on food at home. NEVER tell a child people will not love him if he is fat or if he will not eat.

PETER had a weight problem and he knew it was because he was constantly nibbling all day long, his life was one long snack whether he felt hungry or not. At times of great stress he indulged in secret panicky binges, eating everything he could lay hands on. During a course of therapy it came to light that as an infant his mother would leave him with a bottle instead of cuddling him affectionately when he was being fed, and this had permanently affected him emotionally. Unconsciously as an adult he associated feeding with love and had a deep longing for both.

An early sign of eating problems to look out for is when a child gets fat but never appears to eat at the table. He could be stealing food from the cupboard or even stealing money to buy food or stealing sweets from shops. Such behaviour can start as early as 6 years and will only get worse as the child grows older.

CHAPTER EIGHTEEN

Nobody's Perfect

Let other bards of angels sing bright suns without a spot,
but thou art no such perfect thing rejoice that thou are not.
William Wordsworth

Do you consider yourself perfect in every way? If you answer yes to that question, you certainly have no need to be reading this book, in fact there is little point in your being on this earth at all. Nobody is perfect and hardly anyone comes anywhere remotely near it, so why are you so worried about having faults? It is a fact that many people with eating problems also have very high standards. They set themselves almost impossible standards by which to live their lives and when they fail, as they inevitably will, to live up to them, the result is disappointment, guilt and the inevitable bingeing. Everyone needs certain standards to prevent them drifting through life on a downward spiral, but these should always be reasonable and attainable.

Eating standards

You have an eating problem, you have a problem with your weight. Do you intend to live on a rigid diet for every hour of every day for the rest of your life? Everyone has their good days and their bad days, their times of achievement and their periods of failure; your life has been like that so far and will continue that way. So there are going to be days when you eat more, weeks when you put on a little weight, but there will also be times when you eat less and the pounds disappear.

A rigid routine that never allows you a little leeway is asking for trouble; a non-stop strict diet for a long period of time is just too much to ask of your body and your will-power, inevitably you will end up with a binge. Be realistic and listen to your body, on those days when you really feel more hungry, eat more and on those days when something so wonderful happens that you forget about eating, eat a little less, but remember, don't skip any meals.

Living standards

The same rule of only making your standards reasonable applies to everything you do. Don't set yourself the task of decorating the whole house in one day. It can't be done, a professional decorator would take a fortnight. You will soon discover that you have taken on far more than you can reasonably expect to achieve and so you will probably give up and binge instead. Much better to aim at one room over a weekend, hard going but quite possible to do and to achieve a result of which you can be proud.

When you have achieved something, be satisfied with it, don't pick at little things to spoil it whether it is one speck of paint on the window after you have decorated, or one apple too many when you have been sticking to your eating plan without bingeing.

Slimming standards

You look at yourself in the mirror and shudder. You try and do the zip up on your jeans and despair. Suddenly you want to be slim immediately. You set yourself the impossible task of losing a stone before the weekend or 5 stone before your summer holiday which is only weeks away.

You must realise you won't achieve it; as soon as the message gets home that you won't be slim and slender overnight, the misery sets you off on another binge and those jeans are even tighter next time you try them on. Instead put them away in a drawer and say you are not going to get them out for three months, by which time you might have lost enough weight to do them up with ease.

Don't set yourself a rigid and boring diet and think you will stick to it without faltering every day. When you get tempted by a passing cream bun you will feel so disappointed in yourself for failing to stick to that high standard of dieting that you will eat another bun, and another one.

Recognising the limitations

It is important to recognise your own limitations, you know what they are even if you will not admit to them. You know that you binge, but you also know that you don't binge all the time, that there are times when you can overcome it. Accept the fact that you are able to get your eating under control, but at the same time realise that it will not happen overnight and you are still likely to binge occasionally.

Don't impose too high a standard on yourself, and don't impose your high standards on others. Just as you are being constantly disappointed in yourself for your failures, you will constantly be disappointed in others if you set them on too high a pedestal or expect them to achieve more than they are truly capable of.

Many compulsive eaters are women who are disappointed in their husbands. Perhaps he has not gone as far in his career as she hoped, he is not earning as much money as she thinks he is capable of doing, or he is just not as interesting and exciting as the man she thought she had married. She has imposed her own high standards on him, without really seeing him clearly, and is disappointed because he has failed to live up to her ambitions. She expresses her frustration by eating.

Does it matter?

Does it really matter if you fail to reach those standards of perfection? If you are sticking to a sensible eating plan, does it really matter if you go over the top occasionally? You have not failed unless you use that one slip up as an excuse for giving up completely.

And who does it matter to if you digress from your own personal path of perfection? Nobody else will mind, or even notice the occasional failure on your part. If they do notice, they will probably be quite glad to discover you are really quite human after all and not some kind of machine that can't go wrong.

The teenager who starves and binges and frets and worries because she has set herself an ideal of being as thin as a top model is trying to please nobody but herself. Her mother would much rather she joined in family meals and did not cry in her bedroom all the time. If she has a boyfriend he would much rather she was fun to be with than ultra skinny.

DIERDRE was a compulsive eater who set herself impossible standards of slimness, which she always failed to maintain and was continually moaning, unhappy and bingeing because she could not reach her ideal weight and maintain it. She said her husband had said he wanted her to be slim, but when questioned her husband admitted he only said he wanted her to be slim so that Dierdre would be content and they could have some peace and quiet about the subject.

The truth is that other people don't even notice if you are a few pounds overweight, unless of course you are continually pointing it out and drawing their attention to it. Everyone has something that they think is wrong with them, even top film stars whose looks are the envy of the world are usually obsessed with some flaw that only they can see. Lots of people worry that their nose is too big or their ears stick out, but others just accept that person's looks and don't see anything wrong unless that person is always talking about the size of their nose or the shape of their ears.

There is no such thing as the perfect figure. Girls with long slim legs moan that they have no bust, petite girls grumble that they are too short, dark girls grumble that they are not blonde, blondes complain that they don't tan in the sun, girls with straight hair want to have curly hair, curly heads want to be straight ... the list goes on and on and on. So don't be too critical of your own figure, don't set yourself too high a standard of perfection in looks. The way you behave and the amount of happiness you have in your life is much more important than the way you look.

> JANE was a very pretty girl. People noticed and admired her lovely face, but she was obsessed by the size of her feet. She was always going on about how big they were, drawing everyone's attention to them, and so of course people noticed that her feet were unusually large, something they would have been unlikely to have spotted if it had not been pointed out.

Even if you achieved a slim figure, got to the top in your career, always managed to keep the house clean and tidy, you would not be satisfied even then because you would be setting yourself ever higher mountain sides to scale. And if you have sacrificed good relationships and happy times to achieve these ambitions, you will not be satisfied because your life will still not be perfect in every respect. Sometimes it is necessary to settle for second best in some things, and if that means being a few pounds overweight for the sake of harmony in the home that is a standard that can be lowered.

Aim high but not over the top, set yourself a target but don't become obsessed by it.

Don't take it personally

Other people also set themselves high standards, you are not alone in wanting everything perfect and immediate. It is particularly important to remember this when others criticise you. You take criticism as a personal attack, you feel rejected and put down because someone else points out that you are less than perfect, that you fail to come up to the ideal standard.

In such a situation never be too quick to blame yourself for failure, to agree with the critic that you have failed in your standards, because in some cases that criticism can be a hidden form of compliment. For example, your friend has been listening to your agonies about your eating problems for years, and secretly feeling quite smug because she does not have a problem like yours, it boosts her confidence to be able to support you and give you advice. Then you decide to make some big changes in your life, you really get your eating under control, achieve a good figure and begin blossoming out socially, perhaps meet a nice boyfriend. You no longer need to lean on your friend, you have a better figure than her, you are more attractive, more popular, and have proved your strength of character. It is only human nature that she will secretly want to bring you down. She will be a saint if she praises your efforts and feels glad for you. More likely she will say you look old and scraggy because you have lost weight, that your boyfriend is really a thoroughly bad lot.

Your new standards, if you begin to succeed at getting your eating under control and building a new life, will be the source of jealousy in others who are still stuck in their old ways that they are dissatisfied with; you will show their standards up as lower than your own. Once on the path of success, never let other people who may come to think of you as a threat allow you to lower the new standards you have discovered.

CHAPTER NINETEEN

The Media Image

> The Worldly Hope men set their Hearts upon
> Turns Ashes – or it prospers; and anon,
> Like Snow upon the Desert's dusty Face,
> Lightning a little Hour or two – is gone.
> Omar Khayyam

Television is perhaps the greatest influence on the majority of people these days. Almost every home has at least one set, not to mention a video, and houses where the television is not switched on every day are definitely in the minority.

Like anything that exerts an influence, it has its greatest power over those who lack the ability to make the best of their lives, those with problems they are unable to face up to, those with eating problems. Television is the ultimate alternative to real life, the easy option that blanks out the problems temporarily.

Television wields its influence in two ways. Firstly, the habit of sitting in front of the set becomes a way of life that is less than satisfying, and secondly, the images that are projected through programmes, and in particular, through television advertising, greatly influence people's thought patterns and living habits. Other forms of advertising, such as magazines, newspapers, packaging and hoardings, all contribute to the bombardment of consumer brainwashing which is an integral part of our modern consumer society. We may think we take it all for granted, but everyone is being influenced all the time at a subconscious level by what we see and hear.

Why do you watch television?

Do you watch television because you really enjoy it and there is nothing else in life you would rather be doing? If so, go ahead and do this thing which gives you so much pleasure. It probably won't do you any harm, and you won't be a person that binges in front of the television. Do you sit in front of the television because you feel too exhausted to make the effort to do anything else? In that case, look at your sleep patterns, your work commitments and your nutrition; if you are regularly that tired out, there is something wrong with your life-style or health. Are you bingeing to give your exhausted body a boost or to compensate for the pleasures you feel you are missing out on?

Do you watch television because you can't think of anything better to do? In that case, you are probably bored and highly likely to binge. Shake yourself out of the television habit today and find something else to occupy you.

Do you sit in front of the television night after night because your husband and family do the same? Is this the only way you can share their company? If so, you have let them get into the habit of taking you for granted. They could all benefit from a change, but if they flatly refuse to change their ways, make the break on your own.

Do you stay at home and watch television because you can't afford to go out? In that case, have you really got the balance of your life right, or have you taken on too big a mortgage, do you really need to save for that holiday, how much are you spending on food?

The disappearance of family life

The television has such a strong hold on our lives because in so many homes it is the thing on which all attention is focused; it does all the entertaining and most of the talking. Social communication has been suffocated because the television is always on. Meal times, in particular, have suffered. No longer is the main meal of the day a time when the family gather around the table to talk, argue, discuss and communicate. Few modern homes are designed with a separate dining room, and many do not even have a dining table. Instead, meals are eaten around the television set, people eat and absorb what is on the set rather than eat and give out communication to others, resulting in people becoming either more withdrawn or more frustrated inside.

Eating while watching television means that what goes in through the mouth tends to take second place to what is going in through the eyes and ears. This is a particular danger for those who live alone or spend too much time alone with the television. It is too easy to get into the habit of putting food in the mouth without really being aware of how much they are eating.

The mother who goes to the trouble to cook a meal for her family feels taken for granted if they hardly seem to notice what they are eating because they are so engrossed in the television. She can become resentful if the family walk into the house and switch on the television without even saying 'hello' or making an effort to notice her before the characters on the screen. The wife grows angry inside at the sight of her husband slumped in his armchair in front of the television every evening, ignoring her. She can easily feel she has taken second place to that set in the corner.

Taken over by technology

The television habit can completely ruin a person's social life and eventually isolate them from society. How often does it happen that you won't go out to visit friends because it would mean missing a good film, or turn down the chance of joining an evening class because it clashes with that serial you refuse to miss? The characters dreamed up by television writers become more real than actual friends and neighbours. They are a lot easier and less demanding to know, and those who find relationships difficult grow to prefer the easy shallow friendship of fictional characters.

Watching television is easy. It is one of the easiest things of modern life, and it is always on tap whenever you choose to press that button, from early morning to late at night. Whenever there is something difficult to be done or uncomfortable thoughts are in your head, turning on the television offers an easy alternative. Life becomes passive instead of active, people become watchers rather than participants.

It is hardly surprising that the majority of bingeing takes place in front of the television. How are your television habits?

Checking your television habits

First check the charts you are filling in and note how often you eat when the television is on and how many times do you binge in front of the television. Try writing down notes on your television habits for a week, and what and how much you eat while watching. Note how many programmes captured your attention sufficiently to prevent your thinking about food.

Television is a habit, and so is compulsive eating. Too often the two go together, and if you want to get out of the eating habit you have to get out of the television habit as well and start doing something different with your life.

JANINE was an unmarried school-teacher who was overweight and on a diet. When she was out at work or visiting friends, she found she could eat sensibly and stick to her diet, but the problem arose when she came home from school to her empty flat. She would come in and put on the television, then start eating cake and doughnuts which caused her a lot of anxiety.

By looking at her charts it was soon obvious that her problem only arose at 4.30 pm, and when she was watching television: that was the only occasion when she let herself go on unplanned food like ice cream, chocolate and biscuits. Obviously, she knew she was going to binge beforehand, otherwise she would not have had those items in the house, so she had mentally set herself up for it during the day. She was persuaded to get rid of her television, and this really changed her life. She started going to evening classes and doing constructive things instead of sitting down in front of the set on her own and she found it much easier to control her eating and lose weight.

If you say you have not got the time to do any of the things recommended in other chapters of this book, such as exercise daily, joining a class or visiting friends, look at your day and see how many hours you spend watching television. If you are short of time, how do you find so many hours to spend in front of the set?

Do you feel weary during the day? Too tired to eat breakfast or prepare a proper lunch, so you nibble and buy snacks all the time? Maybe you are staying up too late watching those late-night films and chat shows. Try switching off the set and going to bed earlier.

Switching on the set can get to be a habit; it's so easy to press a button and turn on entertainment and turn off problems and responsibilities. If it is that little bit less easy to press the switch, you may think twice before switching on. Try putting the set away in a cupboard where it will involve an effort to get it out.

Try completing Chart 19.1 for one week.

You can live without television

Could you live without your television set? Probably the thought secretly horrifies you because a house without a television set is peaceful enough to bring you face to face with emotions, relationships and problems that are being drowned out at the moment. Try turning the television off and see what happens. How do you feel? What response do you get from the rest of the household? Can you cope with the full force of their attention which has been directed elsewhere for so long?

In extreme cases, where the television is directly associated with binges, the only answer is to get rid of the television set completely and force yourself to fill your time in other ways.

If you say it is your family who insist on having the television on, ask yourself if you would not have the set on anyway if they were not there. Why not arrange to go out or into another room

Chart 19.1 Television chart

	Monday	Tuesday	Wednesday	Thursday	Friday	Saturday	Sunday
1) Total of programmes or part-programmes watched							
2) How many were so enjoyable you did not think about food at all?							
3) How many did you watch for the sake of having the television on?							
4) How many did you watch because it was easier than doing something else?							
5) How many did you watch when you would rather have had a conversation?							
6) How many times did you put off going out because you wanted to watch a programme?							
7) How many times did you watch television because you felt too tired to do anything else?							
8) How many times did you sit and watch television because it was the only way to be with your family?							
9) How many times did advertising influence your choice of food?							
10) How many times did you binge while watching?							

while they are watching their programmes, or take up a creative hobby such as needlework, painting or even jigsaw puzzles that will keep your mind and hands occupied?

Television is just another addiction. Serial writers shape their scripts to get you tuning in again for the next episode, that is the way they earn their living, like the drug pusher who makes his money by ensuring the addict will always want to come back for more. Compared with many things, television is only a mild form of addiction. If you find something more creative and sociable to do instead of watching 'Crossroads', it is surprising how quickly you cease to think about what is going on in that particular serial. Miss a few episodes and you are quickly broken of the habit until you happen to switch on again and pick up the old threads.

Breaking the habit of switching on the set is more difficult. Observe when you switch on and why. Do you do it through habit at a certain time every day, or only when you feel bored or lonely or troubled? Is it because you urgently want to see a particular programme, or does it go on no matter what is showing just because it talks to you and moves and entertains in a way real people in your life are failing to do?

The power of advertising

Sandwiched between the programmes come the advertisements, and a large proportion of these are for food products, continually encouraging viewers to eat, eat, eat. What could be worse for someone already battling with an eating problem? It is the responsibility of the advertising agency to sell their client's product, and they don't spend huge amounts of money on television advertising unless they can be fairly sure their message will get across.

Advertising probably influences people's lives more than any other one thing, and yet it is in the hands of people whose first concern is to make money, rather than improve the quality of the lives of those they influence. Because we live in a society that is ruled by trade and commerce we have to live with the by-products of such a way of living which are too often material plenty and spiritual famine.

Exercise

Look around your house and through your cupboards and write down a list of things you have bought that you did not really want or need but just because you saw them advertised. It may be a new brand of fish soup advertised on television with a catchy tune which the family would not touch (you know they all hate anything with fish in), or it may be that gadget that looked so handy when you saw a demonstration in the store, but you used it once, and never took it out of the cupboard again. Also, consider how many times you have felt deprived because you could not buy something you saw advertised, from a new house to a tiny bikini. How many times have your children pestered you to buy toys or sweets because they have seen them advertised?

Big money fights big money at the top, and somewhere down below women with food problems are caught up in the crossfire. Millions are spent promoting sweets and millions more promoting slimming products. Volumes are written on how to lose weight and volumes on how to create rich puddings and bake cakes. What one advertising whizz-kid bends all his wits to promoting, another will work equally hard discrediting. No wonder we are confused.

Advertising is a fundamental part of our lives. Without advertising there would be no television, no magazines, no newspapers, and many other events, and sporting fixtures would disappear without the sponsorship of the big companies. But to come to grips with the problem of what to buy and what not to buy, the consumer must always remember that she is ruthlessly being used by advertisers to persuade her to spend her money. The compulsive eater must never forget that in real life a bar of chocolate will not help you to get through your daily life with a smile, it will add inches to your thighs, and rot your teeth. But if the ad. men told you that, you would not spend your money on their product.

The Siren's song

There are many legends of beautiful women who sang sweet

songs to sailors to lure their ships on to the rocks. The Siren song of the advertising men is just as deadly; it promises everything you ever wanted, just there for the taking. Those happy families in the ads have beautiful homes, spotlessly clean and superbly equipped. Those slender models eat chocolate and cakes and trifles and still keep their ultra-thin figures.

It is all an illusion, a beautiful picture of how we would like our world to be. There is no such thing as instant anything, to imply that all you want is just there for the taking merely breeds discontent, envy and a warped view of life. Those models never dare touch a morsel of chocolate in real life. It is more than their jobs are worth to spoil their figures or their complexions. The average family has to work and save for years to achieve a nice house, a car, smart furniture and a tidy flowering garden.

Try watching those television advertisements in a new light. As each one comes up on the screen, analyse what emotional buttons it is pressing inside you. How are you reacting? Does the image of the product being projected reflect something you feel is lacking in your life?

Love or meat pies

A frozen chicken pie has little character or personality of its own, so it has to be given an image that people can associate with. A scene of a happy, loving family seated round a table, adoring their mother for serving them up this pie creates that image; if you react to it, are you really reacting to the pie or to the scene? If you have that warm family atmosphere around your table, it does not matter whether they are eating bread and butter or caviar and champagne, and heating up a frozen pie will certainly not create that atmosphere if it is missing. Again, television is offering the easy alternative. No need to build up a deep, caring relationship with your family, just defrost a chicken pie.

Of course, the same applies to food habits, eat instead of facing problems, serve a meal instead of building a relationship. It's just not that easy.

You can't have everything you want

It's an unpopular message in this age of plenty, and one that goes very much against what we are being told every day by the media. But if you want to improve your life, to get your eating under control, you have got to draw up a balance sheet of priorities. What do you really want out of life? Do you really want to be slim, or do you actually want to be able to eat anything you want, in which case, you must face up to having a weight problem? Do you really want a good social life and a happy relationship with your family or do you really want to carry on nursing your hang-ups and your grievances that form a barrier between you and the rest of the world?

Playing the advertising game

To outwit the advertisers and play them at their own game takes a mind as tortuous as those that dream up the original images, and earns a lot of money for doing so. Advertising is a well-researched and expertly applied science of the mind. The advertisers know exactly how to get through to potential customers and they have few scruples about doing so.

American figures show a typical video-viewing child or teenager will be exposed to between 8,000 and 13,000 commercials advertising processed foods and beverages each year. Over 50 per cent of money spent on television advertising is directed at interesting children in junk food.

There is no obligation on the advertisers to stress what makes up a healthy diet, remember their one and only aim is to sell the product for the manufacturer. Although legislation is constantly trying to tighten up on the advertisers and force them to give the public the straight facts, the media men keep coming up with still more subtle ways of bending the truth to suit their product. Even when it comes to listing the ingredients in a packet or tin, it is still important to read the labels very carefully. Is the number of calories given per packet or per 100 grammes? Are the nutritionally beneficial ingredients there in any great proportion, or are they merely mentioned at the foot of a long list of junk ingredients?

Consider the food items that are advertised on television, nearly all of them are manufactured products, and the bigger the manufacturer, the more money he can afford to spend promoting his product, regardless of whether it merits being more popular than another. Millions are spent on careful packaging, layout of supermarkets, magazine and television advertising, and generally promoting a desirable image for the product, and the more money that is spent the more people are influenced.

Most of the highly advertised products are ones that we could all live quite happily without, they are not essential, but it is up to the ad men to convince us that they are. Tinned, packaged and processed foods are the ones that are remorselessly pushed by the advertisers with no regard to the bad effects it could have on people, particularly those who have eating problems and need dissuading from eating such products rather than persuading to consume them. There is a disproportionate emphasis on snacks, sweets and soft drinks, things that are easy to buy and easy to eat, like cakes, biscuits, pies and frozen tasty dishes are exactly the kinds of foods that go to make up a binge.

The compulsive eater, with all her emotional problems adding to her eating problems, is a sure target for unscrupulous advertising, and if she allows herself to spend too much time in front of the television, exposed to this kind of advertising, she is doing herself a serious disfavour.

Advertisers know that if they want to put a message across they need to repeat it often, which is why you might see the same advertisement repeated several times during one evening. The compulsive eater knows the power of repetition. If she has been told time and again during her life that she is fat and stupid, she comes to believe it of herself.

Some tricks of the trade

A good sales technique is to package items in large quantities so customers cannot buy a single item, or are told they can save money by buying double the quantity. This, of course, does not apply to the compulsive eater who will eat twice as much if she has bought it. This technique generally encourages people to eat more than they really need or originally intended. Never buy more than you need, you will not keep it in the cupboard for another day, you know you will eat it all on your next binge. Putting displays of chocolates and sweets at the check-out is a strong temptation to shoppers while they are waiting in the queue. Good for sales, but bad for eating problems. Try and choose a check-out without such a display, even if it means going to a different supermarket, otherwise try turning your back on the sweets, or striking up a conversation with the person next to you to take your mind off them.

Supermarkets are very carefully planned to get the customers to spend as much money as possible. The only way to outwit them is to write a shopping list before you go out and stick strictly to it; avoid any urge to impulse buy. Also, never go shopping when you are feeling hungry or emotionally upset, as you will be tempted to buy binge foods. Recognise that packaging is designed to catch the eye and make you buy. A carrot, still muddy from the ground, does not look as attractive as a glossy pack of salted peanuts if you feel like a snack, and water from the tap has far less consumer appeal than a brightly coloured can of fizzy drink, it also has a lot less calories. Be aware of the power of advertising, and be on your guard. At a time when you are feeling good, write down a list of permitted snacks and carry it with you, then if you feel you have to buy something, get out your list and only choose something from that, such as a juicy piece of fruit.

The ideal image

Advertisers don't have time to go into detail, they have to put their message over in a few seconds, and so they use the tried and tested stereotypes that television viewers have been trained to recognise at a glance, the cute kid, the protective father, the slim girl, the comic fat lady.

Advertisers deal in images, they are looking for the ideal image to capture the attention of viewers and they make great use of the image of the slender female. The slim woman eats chocolate, is romanced, adored, happy, fulfilled – she is everything every woman secretly wishes to be. This so often results in women dieting and losing weight because they believe they will achieve everything they desire when they too are slim, but when they reach that ideal weight and their life has not improved they carry on dieting and being obsessed with their weight, still searching for that elusive image.

The image of the very slim woman is largely a product of the twentieth century. In earlier centuries, although the woman was regarded as inwardly frail, she tended to be plump and motherly to give an image of fertility. At different times during history fashions were padded and artificially filled out to give the impression of full hips or ample bosoms.

The slender woman of history was usually an image given to the product of male fantasy, the *femme fatale* rather than the wife and mother. But in the twentieth century women threw off their restricting and disguising clothes and also their maternal image. The slender image says, I am my own person, not someone else's wife or mother. The slender image is a symbol of liberation. But true liberation is from within, an attitude of mind and an ability to come to terms with the demands of life. Without the inner qualities to give it substance the outer image is just a mirage. There cannot be a liberated body without a liberated mind.

So the search for a slim figure must also include the discovery of a complete person, otherwise it is all as shallow and meaningless as believing that opening a tin of baked beans for your family will bring you their instant love and respect.

CHAPTER TWENTY

Sabotage and Motivation

The Road to Freedom is through Laughter.
Eric Berne

Life is a serious business. All sorts of disasters loom up continually and ghastly pitfalls appear just when everything seems to be going smoothly for once. It is too easy to be miserable and gloomy about failures, to give up in the face of problems and take the easy way out because it all seems such a joyless struggle. It is at such times that it is easiest to sabotage one's best efforts, while in light-hearted moments it is much easier to feel well-motivated and determined to struggle on.

Being able to laugh at situations is essential, and so is the ability to laugh at yourself and the stupid things you see yourself doing every day. Seek out the company of people who seem to laugh a lot. Their humour is infectious and half an hour in their company will re-establish your perspective of events and strengthen your motivation. Watch a funny programme on television, or read a funny book, and always try to see the funny side of every situation – there usually is one if you look hard enough. Wallowing in gloom is the quickest way to sabotage your efforts. Motivation is the driving force that keeps you heading along the road you have set yourself. It is the enthusiasm with which you do anything, from the smallest daily chore to organising the complete pattern of your life, and it will determine the amount of energy you give each project and the ultimate success you achieve. Sabotage is the deliberate stumbling blocks you put in that road to slow your progress or make you give up and turn back.

Logically it would seem that everyone would try to do the best for themselves all the time and work towards making their life as easy and successful as possible. Yet every single person without exception at some time sabotages their own best efforts. There is some seed of self-destruction in each of us that makes us do things that are against our better interests. It could be the clever child who deliberately makes mistakes in his school work because he does not want his friends to think he is brighter than them. It could be the girl who breaks up with a boyfriend she adores because she is afraid one day he might stop being as affectionate towards her as he is now.

Compulsive eaters are continually sabotaging their own efforts to overcome their eating and weight problems. Often they just do not give themselves a chance to prove they can get their life under control. Sometimes it is done deliberately, often it is unintentional. Many times they set themselves standards that are far too high, they know they will not achieve them and so failure is built in as the end result of their efforts.

FIONA could not think what to get her dad as a present on father's day, so in the end she went out and bought him a big box of her favourite chocolates, knowing chocolates are her great weakness. Of course, she ate the whole box on her way home and her father never received his present.

DEIDRE bought her friend a tin of biscuits as a Christmas present. Even though she knew how often she got cravings for biscuits, she bought the present in October and put it away in her wardrobe. For two months she battled against the desire to binge on those biscuits and eventually ate the lot on Christmas Eve when she got the tin out to wrap it up.

ROSE thought she would join an evening class to get her out of the house and away from her eating problems. (So she enrolled for a cake icing course!)

Time and again people with eating problems embark on the eating plan, understanding the importance of regular protein meals and the need to keep blood sugar levels stable. They appreciate that eating has to be controlled first, after which weight problems can be tackled gradually. They then go out and

194

buy a dress that is too small for them for an important event the following week and go on a crash diet thinking they will slim down enough to wear it.

Are they deliberately trying to sabotage their good attempts to overcome their eating problems? Or are they just not properly motivated to get their eating under control? There are a lot of pay-offs for the emotionally unstable in being a compulsive eater, and these can be a powerful force behind a behaviour that would logically seem absurd. It can be used to avoid sexual relationships, even as an excuse for not going out and making friends when the real reason is lack of confidence. It is easier to say, 'I haven't got any friends because I binge' than to say 'I haven't got any friends because I find it impossible to be friendly towards other people.' Compulsive eating can also be used to punish others, a husband who spends too much time at work or a parent who makes too much of a fuss about eating habits. It can be used as an excuse for failing exams where a sense of failure is too difficult to live with. 'I failed because I spent too much time bingeing instead of working for my exams,' is easier to live with than 'I failed because I am too lazy to study and not clever enough to understand the work.'

When bingeing provides such a comfortable excuse for so many things, no wonder many compulsive eaters say they are not prepared to give up their bingeing unless they can be guaranteed life will be happy and trouble free when their eating is under control. This is where motivation comes in, the belief that what you are working to achieve is worthwhile and that the quality of life will be improved when deep-seated problems have been confronted. The right motivation will override the instinct to sabotage.

Some people seem to be highly self-motivated right from the start, just as some people are born without weight problems. But for the majority it is a continual struggle to keep that driving force fired and ticking over. Enthusiasm needs regular booster injections because it gets used up in the wear and tear of everyday living.

There is that day when you start off determined to beat your eating problems, some particular incident, perhaps reading this book, has motivated you to make the effort and you are full of enthusiasm and high hopes. But before long problems start coming along, familiar emotional problems send you running to the food cupboard, you are surrounded by temptations to eat too much of the wrong things. Your motivation weakens and falters and you find yourself bingeing again.

First of all, accept the fact that this is going to happen. If you were the sort of person who was strong-willed and self-motivated enough to carry such an ambitious programme through from start to finish without faltering, it is unlikely you would have an eating problem in the first place. Secondly, make plans in advance for those times of inevitable weakness. A second line of defence that will reinforce your motivation.

What motivates you?

Have you ever worked out what motivates you to do things? Think back over the things you have achieved in your life and work out what was the driving force behind that success.

Anger is a very strong motivator. If you are sufficiently angry with yourself over your eating habits, you will have the motivation to really do something about them. But if anger is your driving force be very careful, this is a dangerous and destructive emotion if not handled with extreme caution and directed carefully.

Shame is another great driving force. If you look in the mirror and really feel ashamed of the way you look and the way you live your life, this can push you into making changes. The urge to show all those people who have been putting you down all your life that you can make something of yourself can be turned into a very positive creative force, but shame can also be turned inward and become guilt which will drag you down.

Falling in love is perhaps the most powerful motivator of all. People can achieve miracles while their heads are in the clouds of romance, but how disastrous it can be if you fall back to earth with a sudden bump. The first thing you reach for is food.

So if a strong emotion is your motivation, handle it with extreme care. It is like a wild animal which has to be kept constantly under control, because at any moment it can turn and inflict a nasty injury on you.

What motivates other people?

Other people always seem to be so well motivated, they are all out there doing and achieving while you seem to be the only one who can't make it. The answer to that is that very few people are any more motivated than the rest. It is just that outsiders only see the things others achieve, while their doubts and failures are kept hidden. How many people know about *your* problems, your failures, your eating habits?

Making changes

What things in your life can you change, and what things is it impossible to alter?

There is no point wearing yourself down with despair because you are 4 feet 8 inches tall instead of 5 feet 6 inches. This is something inherited through generations of your family and you have to accept it. You also have to accept that your metabolic rate is in part an aspect of your inherited make-up and if you are the sort of person who puts on weight easily, you are never going to become a person who can eat as much as she likes and always stay slim.

Then there are the things which you can change if you are really obsessed about them, like the shape of your nose or the way your ears stick out. Plastic surgery is available if you have the money and a really drastic problem. Bust operations and bottom lifts are fairly drastic measures, possibly acceptable for film stars who can earn millions with the shape of their bodies, but for anyone else they only reflect an inner dislike of themselves. The problem then is a psychological rather than a physical one.

For the average woman, her basic shape and proportions are the ones she is stuck with for life, and the best thing to do is accept it and come to terms with anything you think is less than ideal. Learn to love your body. But what you then do with that basic shape in the way of unnecessary fat, loose muscles, bad skin and untidy hair and nails is very much in your power to change, and if you love your body you will want to make the best of it.

Exercise
Name two things about yourself that you cannot change. Name two things about yourself that you can change. Ask yourself why you are not motivated to change them at the moment (answer truthfully).

Excuses, excuses

'I have lost weight before but never manage to lose it from my stomach which is where I really want it to go from. Why should I bother to try again?': dieting alone is not enough, especially if you have quite a bit of weight to lose. It is essential to exercise at the same time so that the fat cells are encouraged to disappear from those areas where they settle most comfortably. A flabby stomach probably means flabby muscles, so get those tummy muscles working and back into shape so by the time you are at your ideal weight you will no longer have that old problem.

'All my problems come from my being overweight. If I had a firm flat stomach I would be happy, but I can't control my eating enough to get slim.': is being overweight the true source of unhappiness? Is it not more accurate to say that unhappiness is the source of being overweight; eating problems often stem from emotional problems. Inability to face up to the true reason for your eating problems makes it easy to hide behind figure faults. You will never get and stay slim because you have no true motivation to remove this convenient emotional shelter. If you worked hard at achieving a flat stomach and achieving a slim figure and your relationship with your husband was no better or your ability to do your job did not improve, what then could you blame your unhappiness on?

For motivation to work it has to be based on an honest assessment of yourself. Your driving force has to be what you truly feel and not some convenient excuse you have made up to avoid facing up to reality. If you feel you are good at being a compulsive eater, ask yourself why you are so successful at it. There are people who need to be compulsive eaters, just as there are people who need to be ill, because it is something they know and feel familiar with. It is a condition they can just about handle, while problems of the outside world are strange, difficult and frightening.

Saying and doing

People are saying things all the time, they are constantly telling themselves and others about all the things they are going to do and achieve. But with so many people, especially those who talk a lot, what they say and what they do are two very different things.

Compulsive eaters always say they want to sort out their lives, lose weight and get their eating under control, but there are always these insurmountable difficulties, these continual obstacles that prevent them from getting started. In fact these are just excuses that offer them the easy way out.

It is the easiest thing in the world to blame other people and outside circumstances for your failures. But everybody has free choice in the way they live their lives, and everybody finds the time, the energy and the motivation to achieve the things which are really important to them. The compulsive eater may say she is hard up, but she always finds the money for food. She says she is busy but always finds the time to eat. If you have not got your eating under control, it is because, deep down inside, perhaps you do not really want to. If you honestly want your eating to be under control and that is really the most important thing in your life, somehow you *will* find the motivation.

Strengthening the resolve

Telling yourself, and believing, that you want to get your eating under control is something you should be doing constantly. Not just saying it with your mouth, but meaning it with your heart and soul.

Exercise 1

When you wake up in the morning say to yourself: 'just for today, I will not binge'; or 'just for today, I will not weigh myself'; or 'just for today I will eat regular meals'.

Whichever of these you choose for the day, keep saying it to yourself and write it down at least once every half hour. Just for today. Tomorrow will have a new challenge, this is your battle for today.

Exercise 2

When you feel the urge to eat something you know you should not: stop.

Press the tip of each thumb against the side of the index finger of the same hand, just by the base of the nail, and hold the point firmly.

Take a deep breath.

Continue breathing slowly and deeply while you count slowly to ten. Deep slow breathing helps you to concentrate on relaxing. You are probably starting to breathe quickly at the thought of eating.

If you still feel agitated repeat the slow breathing while you count to ten again. Now consider calmly and rationally whether you really need to eat just at this moment. Could you not put it off for half an hour?

If you succeed in delaying your eating for just half an hour, the success might motivate you to extend that time until you reach a proper meal, but don't expect to succeed every time. Let failure be the motivation to succeed next time.

Exercise 3

Take a large sheet of blank paper and rule a line down the centre. On the left-hand side of the page, write a positive statement that you feel is relevant to your particular problem, mentioning yourself by name. Then on the right-hand side of the page, write down the first reply that comes into your head. When you have finished return to the left-hand column and repeat your original statement, then on the right put down the next reply that comes into your head. Continue until you run out of replies. It is important to repeat this exercise at the same time each day. At the end of the week, read through your answers and see what you have learnt from them. Your page might look something like this:

I, Jane Smith, don't eat chocolate biscuits because ...	They make me fat.
I, Jane Smith, don't eat chocolate biscuits because ...	I know if I eat one, I will eat the whole packet.

How can other people supply motivation?

Motivation comes mainly from within; it is a personal battle that the compulsive eater has to fight and overcome on her own. But in any battle it is always a help to have someone else alongside, reloading the rifles or at least not attacking from a second direction at the same time.

People who are strong willed and highly motivated themselves may try to impose their strength on the compulsive eater with the best of intentions, but this can cause even more problems if it inspires feelings of guilt or resentment. It is not possible to bully a compulsive eater into changing her eating habits, but if she has made a start on a programme of self-help she can be encouraged and supported in a practical way.

If you know someone with an eating problem, encourage her to join you when you take the dog for a walk or go out jogging. Agree to join an aerobics class together and call round to collect her before each class. Have the time to listen at the end of the telephone if she is at a crisis, but be firm and don't allow yourself to become a crutch for her to lean on at every little shortcoming.

Try and be the daily boost to motivation, and above all never, NEVER make fun of her, even though you may mean it as a friendly joke. Remember she is oversensitive about her problem and easily put down.

One method that has been tried by marriage guidance and

child guidance counsellors to sort out problems between members of families is the idea of making a contract.

Exercise

A husband and wife agree on a contract that involves give and take on both sides and involves a situation that is causing tension between them and causing the wife, who has eating problems, to binge.

For example, the wife finds it difficult to stop herself eating high-calorie foods because he wants chips with every meal and a pudding every day. She is also resentful because he goes off every Saturday afternoon to play football and then on to the pub with the boys.

Their contract might say that he agrees to eat a more sensible diet during the week which will not only be better for him but will help her stick to her eating plan. In return she will not show any resentment or make a scene when he goes out on Saturdays. If the root of the wife's eating problems lie in her relationship with her husband, this kind of contract can be very useful because it helps both partners to appreciate the negative emotions that are being aroused.

The money motive

Money is always a powerful motive to do anything. Think how well off you would be if you never spent money on binge foods. Work out honestly how much money you spend on binge food in a month, then each time you feel you might have binged but were able to handle the situation, you can calculate the savings in pounds and pence. Actually put away the amount of money you would have used for bingeing when you get paid or are given your housekeeping money. Put it in a box and tell yourself you will not use it for binge foods because you are not going to binge. At the end of the month if you still have the money and have not 'borrowed' from it for bingeing, go out and spend it all on something luxurious for yourself, like a new dress or a hairdo.

The answer within

Although there are any number of tricks that can be used to boost motivation, in the end it must come from within. That is where the answer to your eating problems is to be found, because that is where your compulsive eating begins. Nobody else and nothing else can sort out your life for you, it is a task only you can undertake. It is often difficult to keep on doggedly in the company of other people. Our society often does not appreciate achievement and hard work, success is met with much jealousy and bad feeling from others. How often is a hard working employee given the impression by his colleagues that he is 'letting the side down' by achieving more than them? How many times do others try and persuade you not to stick to your diet because they can't be bothered to diet themselves, 'Go on have a piece of cake, we're all having some'?

High achievers are often loners, outcasts from society, and if you tackle the eating plan seriously and dedicate yourself to getting your eating under control you may find while you are doing it that you seem to have little in common with those around you, that you are the only one having to battle and work so hard. Motivation is always higher if you are doing the thing you really want to do, so it is important you get to the roots of what you really want out of life and then start doing it. Think what the people who have really made it to the top have had to sacrifice to get there. Their motivation was the knowledge that they wanted to succeed, they listened to the voice of their own inner knowledge and disregarded what rivals and less highly motivated people told them.

Good luck and good motivation in finding your way out of the Food Trap.

Appendix I   Reading List

Fat Is A Feminist Issue   Susie Orbach, Hamlyn Ltd, 1979

Why Do I Think I Am Nothing Without a Man?   Penelope Russianoff PhD, Bantam Books Inc, 1983

Eating is Okay   Henry A Jordan MD, Leonard S Levitz PhD, Gordon M Kimbrell PhD, Rawson Associates Publishers Inc, 1976

Dieting Makes You Fat   Geoffrey Cannon and Hetty Einzig, Century Publishing Co Ltd, 1983

Women and Fatigue   Dr Marion Hilliard, Pan Books Ltd, 1963

The Dieter's Dilemma   William Bennett MD, and Joel Gurin, Basic Books Inc.

The Body Clock Diet   Ronald Gatty PhD, Simon & Schuster, 1980

Bulimarexia   Marlene Boskind-White PhD, William C White Jr PhD, George J McLeod Ltd.

Body Mind & Sugar   E M Abrahamson MD, and A W Pezet, Holt Rinehart and Winston, 1960

Treat Obesity Seriously   J S Garrow, Churchill Livingstone.

Selfwatching   Ray Hodgson and Peter Miller, Century Publishing Co Ltd, 1982

Sugar Blues   William Dufty, Abacus Press, 1980

Taking the Rough with the Smooth   Dr Andrew Stanway, Pan Books Ltd, 1981

Fit or Fat?   Covert Bailey, Pelham Books Ltd, 1980

The Aerobics Way   Kenneth H Cooper MD MPH, Transworld Publishers Ltd, 1978

A Woman In Your Own Right   Anne Dickson, Quartet Books Ltd, 1982

Let's Eat Right to Keep Fit   Adelle Davis, Unwin Paperbacks, 1984

Not All in the Mind   Dr Richard Mackarness, Pan Books Ltd, 1982

The Composition of Foods   A A Paul and D A T Southgate, Her Majesty's Stationery Office, 1978

Jane Brody's Nutrition Book   W W Norton & Co Inc, 1981

The Sensuous Slimmer   Caroline Buchanan and Sandra Sedgbeer, New English Library, 1984

Competing With the Sylph   L M Vincent MD, Andrews & McMeel Inc.

Low Blood Sugar   Martin Budd, Thorsons Publishers Ltd, 1981

The Premenstrual Syndrome   Caroline Shreeve, Thorsons Publishers Ltd, 1983

Once A Month   Katharina Dalton, Fontana, 1978

Release From Nervous Tension   D H Fink, Unwin Paperbacks, 1984

Futurewoman   Shirley Conran and Elizabeth Sidney, Penguin Books, 1981

Appendix II   Useful Addresses

The following addresses include not only support groups and associations of particular use for those with eating and related problems, but also contacts for alternative therapies, sports associations and voluntary services. In most cases the main contact address is given.

Al-anon	61 Great Dover Street, London SE1 4YE 01 403 0888
Alcoholics Anonymous	01-352 3001 P.O. Box 1, Stonebow House, Stonebow, York YO1 2NJ 0904 644026/7
Anorexic Aid	The Priory Centre, 11 Priory Road, High Wycombe, Bucks. 0494 21431
British Association of Counselling	37a Sheep Street, Rugby EV21 3BX 0788 78328
British Wheel of Yoga	31 Mercian Park Close, Cheltenham, Gloucester 0242 581 336
Brook Advisory Centre for Young People	233 Tottenham Court Road, London W1P 9AE 01 323 1522 01 580 2991
The Centre for Autogenic Training	15 Fitzroy Square, London W1P 5HQ 01 388 1007
Citizen's Advice Bureau Service (CAB) (Greater London)	31 Wellington Street, London WC2E 7DA. 01 828 7022
Community Service Volunteers	237 Pentonville Road, Islington, London N1 9NJ 01 278 6601
The Compassionate Friends (for parents who have lost a child)	6 Denmark Street, Bristol B61 5DO 0272 29970
Consumers Association	14 Buckingham Street, London WC2N 6DS 01 486 5544
Cruse (for widows, widowers and their children)	Cruse House, 126 Sheen Road, Richmond TW9 1UR 01 940 4818/9047

Depressives Anonymous	C/C Keith Middleton, 21 The Green, Cheddersley Corbet, Worcester.
Drug Advisory Services Ltd	SWAPA, 1 Neville Street, Canton, Cardiff 0222 383313/26113
Family Planning Association	27–35 Mortimer Street, London W1A 4QW 01 636 7866
Family Welfare Association	501 Kingsland Road, Dalston, London E8 4AU 01 254 6251
Gamblers Anonymous	17–23 Blantyre Street, London SW10 01 352 3060
Gingerbread (for Single Parents)	35 Wellington Street, London WC2 01 240 0953
Institute of Family Therapy	43 New Cavendish Street, London W1M 7RG 01 935 1651
International Bacchus Organisation (a charitable social organisation for young professionals 20–35)	24 Eccleston Street, London SW1
International Voluntary Services	Ceresole House, 53 Regent Road, Leicester 0533 54 1862 Great Victoria Street, Belfast 0232 238147 1 Upper Parliament Street, Liverpool L8 1TD 051 709 6726 188 Roundhay Road, Leeds 05324 484453
Iyengar Yoga Institute	223a Randolph Avenue, London W9 1NL 01 624 3080
Jogging Association	Westlake Cottage, New Stead, Abbey Park, Nottingham NG15 8GE 0623 79 3496
Mental Health Foundation	8 Hallam Street, London W1N 6DH

Mothers' Action Support Team (Self-help group who aim to combat the loneliness felt by women at home)	18 The Woodlands, Linton, Cambridge
National Advisory Centre on Careers for Women	Drayton House, 30 Gordon Street, London WC1H 0A 01 380 0117
National Association for Mental Health	111 Mycenae Road, London SE3 7XR 01 858 4849
National Association for Mental Health (MIND)	22 Harley Street, London W1N 2ED 01 637 0741
National Association of Women's Clubs	5 Vernon Rise, Kings Cross, London WC1X 9EP 01 837 1434
National Council for the Divorced and Separated	13 High Street, Little Shelford, Cambridge CB2 5ES
National Council for the Single Woman and her Dependants	29 Chilworth Mews, London W2 3RG
National Council for Voluntary Organisations	26 Bedford Square, London WC1B 3HU 01 636 4066
National Federation of Women's Institutes	39 Eccleston Street, London SW1W 9NT 01 380 0117
National Women's Register	The Administrator, 245 Warwick Road, Solihull, West Midlands B92 7AH 021 706 1101
National Marriage Guidance Council	Herbert Gray College, Little Church Street, Rugby, Warwickshire 0788 732 41
Open Door Association (Agoraphobia)	447 Pensey Road, Heswell, Merseyside.
Patients' Association	335 Grays Inn Road, London WC1X 8PX 01 837 7241
Phobic Society	4 Cheltenham Road, Chorlton-cum-Hardy, Manchester M21 1QN 061 881 1937
Relaxation for Living	Danesk, 29 Burwood Park Road, Walton-on-Thames, Surrey, KT12 5LH 0932 22 7826
Release Counselling on Legal, Social and Medical Problems related to drug taking	Emergency (24 hours) 01-603 8654

Samaritans (for Local groups check your telephone directory)	London Branch, St Stephen's Church, 39 Walbrook, London EC4N 8EP
Solo Clubs (for the divorced, widowed or separated)	Room 7/8, Ruskin Chambers, 191 Corporation Street, Birmingham B4 6RY 021 236 2879
The Sports Council	16 Upper Woburn Road, London SW3 01 388 1277
TRANEX (Tranquilliser addiction)	2 St John's Road, Harrow, Middlesex
Voluntary Work Information Services	68 Chalton Street, London NW1 1HJ 01 388 0241
Womens Aid Federation for Battered Wives	374 Grays Inn Road, London WC1 01 837 9316
Workers Educational Association (Adult Education and Social Functions)	32 Tavistock Square, London WC1 0232 49041
Yoga for Health Foundation	Ickwell Bury, Biggleswade, Bedfordshire SG18 9EF

Index

Index

211